COMMUNITY HEALTH ACTION

COMMUNITY HEALTH ACTION

A Study of Community Contrast

by

Paul A. Miller

With the Assistance of J. Allan Beegle,
Duane L. Gibson, Charles R. Hoffer,
Charles P. Loomis, Christopher Sower,
and David G. Steinicke

Michigan State College Press

East Lansing

Without the first interest, constant patience and encouragement,
and financial support of
the Farm Foundation and its Managing Director, Frank W. Peck,
this work would not have been possible.
To such institutions and to such men,
who are frequently the entrepreneurs of social research,
this book is happily dedicated

MANUFACTURED IN THE UNITED STATES OF AMERICA
AT THE LAKESIDE PRESS, R. R. DONNELLEY & SONS COMPANY
CHICAGO, ILLINOIS, AND CRAWFORDSVILLE, INDIANA

TABLE OF CONTENTS

COMMUNITY HEALTH ACTION

FOREWORD

Community Health Action deals with the structure and functioning of the American community pertinent to solving a particular problem. It does not set forth a philosophy of community living, nor does it depict an ideal pattern of organizing and mobilizing the resources of the community toward some desirable goal. This book intentionally overlooks descriptive accounts of community success. Instead, this research report focuses on what really happened when comparable small communities across the land accomplished similar major health goals. The reader will see the elements which contribute to success, but he will also become aware of the problems and anxieties in community action.

There are three elements of strength in this monograph. First, it tries to fill what the authors believe to be important needs in community research: (1) the need for comparative studies of community action toward identical community goals, and (2) the need to relate the community scene to such larger sociocultural systems as the state, region, and nation. The second strength is the use of the decision-making process as the framework for viewing the data upon which the study is based. The third strength is the balanced perspective of an interdisciplinary effort of which this report is but a single product.

A fresh technique used in this work is the use of "event reconstruction" as an approach in community action research. Real difficulties exist in reproducing the historical past. This work attempted to make accurate the reconstruction of past community events by selecting a recent time-span in which the events occurred, by using methods which enabled the recall of informants, and by a continuing cross-check of the methods of interviewing in the field study situation. No less important, and perhaps an innovation, was the use of 287 communities for study, in order that both quantitative and qualitative data about community action could be marshalled toward a specific research purpose.

The evolution of the parent study and of this monograph was truly cooperative. Little could have been accomplished without the sponsorship and financial help together with the wise counsel of representatives of the Farm Foundation, especially the Managing Director, Mr. Frank W. Peck. The Cooperative Extension Service of Michigan State College made available the time of the senior author to serve as chairman of the research committee. Similarly, the Agricultural Experiment Station of Michigan State College made available three staff members to serve on the study committee. The study was developed and carried out within the Social Research Service of Michigan State College.

A great many state and national organizations contributed time, experience, and materials. Of these, special acknowledgment should be made of the counsel obtained from the W. K. Kellogg Foundation, the School of Public Health

3

of the University of Michigan, The Michigan Department of Health, the Farm Credit Administration of the U. S. Department of Agriculture, the Hospital Facilities Division of the U. S. Public Health Service, the National Health Council, and the American Public Health Association.

Obviously, the consultative aid of these organizations and agencies, and the interdisciplinary effort itself were the work of individuals. This project owes much to the interests and contributions of the project committee. Dr. J. Allan Beegle led two research teams to make the case studies in Wyoming and California. Dr. Duane L. Gibson and Mr. David G. Steinicke contributed extensively to the construction and pre-testing of research instruments. Dr. Charles R. Hoffer and Dr. Christopher Sower, with their long experience and practiced insight into community processes, aided materially in the project design and the critical review of the manuscripts.

Acknowledgment is due three other committee consultants. Dr. Edgar A. Schuler, now of Wayne University, assisted greatly the original design of the project. Dr. John Useem aided the committee extensively, in seminar and in the field, in developing an understanding of the decision-making process in relation to community action. Dr. John B. Holland joined the research team in the study of the Alabama community, and participated consequently in many of the discussions relating to the project.

Indispensable steps of any research project are the detailed and unsung planning and testing, coding, tabulation, and field work. For this, three graduate research assistants must receive acknowledgment for their great share in the endeavor: Mr. Joseph H. Locke, Mr. Wayne C. Rohrer, and Mr. Sheldon G. Lowry. Two other graduate students, Mr. Ben Thompson and Mr. Frank Nall, ably joined the research teams for two of the case studies. Miss Helen L. Johnston, U. S. Public Health Service, made many helpful contributions and reviewed a portion of the manuscript. Mrs. Billie Holden superbly managed the clerical and stenographic details throughout the duration of the project.

Finally, there were many citizens, many of whom the project committee will never see, who cooperatively completed questionnaires and withstood intensive interviews. Without them and their interest in a faithful account of events dear to them, there would have been no research at all.

The present monograph adds to a growing body of sociological reporting on health and health facilities by the Social Research Service at Michigan State College. Among the research reports are: *Health and Health Services for Michigan Farm Families*, by Charles R. Hoffer, Special Bulletin 352, AES, Sept., 1948;* "Health and Health Services in Three Michigan Communities," by Charles R. Hoffer, *Quarterly Bulletin*, Vol. 31, Article No. 31–32, AES, August, 1948; "Determination of Unmet Need for Medical Care Among Michigan Farm Families," by Charles R. Hoffer and Edgar A. Schuler, in cooperation with Rosalie Neligh, M.D., and Thomas Robinson, M. D., of the University of Michigan Medical School, printed in the *Journal of the Michigan State Medical Society*, Vol. 46, pp. 443–446, April, 1947; "Objectives and

---

* AES refers to the Agricultural Experiment Station, Michigan State College, East Lansing, Michigan.

Methods of Rural Sociological Research in Health at Michigan State College,"
by Edgar A. Schuler, Charles R. Hoffer, Charles P. Loomis, and Paul A. Miller, *Rural Sociology*, Vol. 14, No. 3, September, 1949; *Mortality Differentials
in Michigan*, by Paul M. Houser and J. Allan Beegle, Special Bulletin 367, AES,
February, 1951; *Distribution of Doctors of Medicine and Osteopaths in Michigan Communities*, by John F. Thaden, Special Bulletin 370, AES, June, 1951;
Health Needs and Health Care in Two Selected Michigan Communities, by
Charles R. Hoffer and Clarence Jane, Special Bulletin 377, AES, June, 1952;
Community Organization for Health: Selected References, by Paul A. Miller,
et al., Social Research Service, December, 1950; and the first comprehensive
study of the unmet medical needs in a state, *Health Needs and Health Care in
Michigan*, by Charles R. Hoffer, Duane L. Gibson, Charles P. Loomis, Paul A.
Miller, Edgar A. Schuler and John F. Thaden, Special Bulletin 365, AES,
June, 1950.

Charles P. Loomis, Ph. D.
Head,
Department of Sociology and Anthropology
Director, Social Research Service

A NOTE ON PROCEDURE *

IN EARLY 1948 Mr. Frank W. Peck, Managing Director of the Farm Foundation, visited with Dr. Charles P. Loomis and the senior author on the campus of Michigan State College. The discussion concerned increasing developments within communities of major health facilities. The result of the meeting was a research project aimed at small community efforts to gain needed health goals. From that day to the present, members of the project committee have been so extraordinarily concerned with method that it is fitting to initiate this report of research with a note on procedure.

A number of limitations were initially imposed: that the study would have an emphasis on the community rather than health; that small towns and rural communities would be of primary interest; that respective community health goals should be of critical importance in small communities; and that the scope of the investigation should be nation-wide. On this arbitrary platform the effort was based.

An exhaustive search of relevant literature and consultations with many cooperative specialists revealed six areas of important health need in small communities: (1) for personnel, such as physicians, nurses, public health workers, and dentists; (2) for hospital facilities; (3) for adequate public health services; (4) for clinics and health centers in very rural areas; (5) for reducing the economic burdens of sickness; and (6) for increased health education. In the interest of making the task manageable, the six areas of need were first reduced to four, and later to three: (1) hospital facilities, (2) public health services, and (3) devices to solve medical and health costs. Since the study proposed to view the aspirations of consumers, the cooperative prepayment plan for medical care was selected as a special device of total consumer sponsorship.

Few would deny that acquiring the three goals would be significant events in the history of any community. The achievement of these facilities is increasingly widespread in small communities. This seemed to make possible a comparative approach. The surge of community health activity since World War II served to insure sufficient cases for orderly research planning. Thus the task was launched.

Throughout 1949 the project committee developed inventories of successful health projects in each of the three problem areas. Unsuccessful projects were ruled out, only after intense debate, because there were insufficient funds to investigate them fully, and because the planned comparisons removed the

* READERS NOTE: Related footnotes and sources, designated by number, will be found in the bibliographical appendix at the end of the book. Supplementary tables, designated by T-1, T-2, etc., will be found in the tabular appendix at the end of the book.

focus from factors of success and lack of success and placed it on the subtleties of community action for differing health goals in wide areas of the United States. Arbitrarily chosen were three criteria for building these inventories: (1) *population*—hospital sites in towns or cities with less than 7,500 population, and health department locations where more than half of the relevant county population was on rural farms; (2) *time*—community action initiated since 1940 in order that local informants would be still available; (3) *type of facility*—new hospital facilities to be general in type or additions to general hospitals, and health departments to be only those providing the six functions of vital statistics, control of communicable diseases, environmental sanitation, laboratory services, maternity, infancy and childhood services, and health education. The rapid expansion of Hill-Burton legislation for hospital construction brought the decision to admit to the inventories only hospital projects that had complied with the provisions of federal legislation.[1]

A perusal of the files of the Hospital Facilities Division, U. S. Public Health Service, yielded 374 projects as of November, 1949, which met the inventory criteria.[2] The *National Directory of Health Officers* was employed in extending an inventory of local health department organizations.[2] These directories, with the 1940 census, revealed 437 departments in counties with more than 50 percent rural farm population. The next step, a postal card questionnaire, elicited from the respective health officers the year of organization and other classification facts. This step provided 115 local health departments meeting both the rurality and time criteria. The inventory of cooperative prepayment plans was courteously provided by officials of the Farm Credit Administration of the U. S. Department of Agriculture. This inventory, in November, 1949, numbered 97 cases—assumed to be all cooperative plans chartered but not necessarily in operation.

As a matter of economy, the questionnaire method was elected. Into this device went months of study, planning, and construction. Many consultations were held with health officials, and 33 community organization specialists aided by suggesting important community action problems in need of solution. This preliminary work resulted in the first draft of a questionnaire. Intermittent visits to Michigan communities kept plans in touch with reality. The first questionnaire was pretested—by personal administration—in three Michigan communities with hospital projects. The resulting second draft of a questionnaire was mailed, again for pretesting, to seven widely separated projects. The responding six provided the third and final draft of the questionnaire, eventually published in booklet form. This is the formal story of the questionnaire. A more informal account would recall July afternoons devoted to wording a single question amid debate, rewriting, and telephone calls to printer and artist. As in all questionnaire construction, this process was graced by a first ethusiasm and ardor, giving way to methodical hours and months of discussion, writing, re-writing, checking, and thorough re-working. To follow the original questionnaire were similar devices for health department organizations and for prepayment plan cases, appropriately varied in style and language.

The questionnaires were transmitted with a personal letter to the official sponsoring agents for inventoried hospital projects, either the presiding official of a hospital board or of a local governing body. For health departments, the letters went to health officers with a request to seek out carefully those most active in the recent organization. Transmission of the prepayment plan questionnaires was similar to that of the hospitals. Three separate mailings were made to each of the three inventories. The first and second mailings included a personal letter and a questionnaire; the third was only a reminder—a final personal note.

The project committee anxiously awaited the result—to be rewarded by 218 responses for hospitals, a 58 percent return;[T-1] 51 responses for health departments, a 45 percent return; and, of the 24 prepayment plans estimated to be operating in November 1949, 18 plans responded, or a percentage return of 75.

Still difficult tasks remained. In addition to the limited data of the questionnaire, the initial plan envisioned some intensive and on-the-ground study. With the usual interplay between funds and staff time, the decision was made so to study only hospital projects. Of these, no more than five could be studied. This decision led eventually to the traditional interest of social scientists in regionalism. Could this solve the problem of case selection? Again, pertinent literature was reviewed and a corresponding analysis of the 218 responding projects was made.

Well-known scholarly regional studies were reviewed. The reporting projects were compared with these on the basis of several regional classifications. These procedures resulted in the selection for operational purposes of Odum's six regions, the Northeast, the Southeast, the Middle States, the Southwest, the Northwest, and the Far West.[3] Important reasons for this choice were that a sixfold classification of the 218 reporting hospital projects permitted sufficient numbers in each category for analysis and comparison, and that the state—combination plan of Odum and his colleagues linked with the projects which were easily identified by state.

It was desired that the hospital projects to be chosen for intensive field study approach the common character of hospital projects within a particular region, rather than the character of small towns in the region. Tabulations of the 218 projects revealed certain regional regularities. Among these were the method of raising funds, the size of goal as indicated by the number of beds in the proposed facility, the total population in the hospital service area, the proportion of rural population, and the degree of unmet hospital need (the ratio of available beds to those needed, according to Hill-Burton estimations). Combinations of these factors were termed "the community situation." Sixteen combinations encompassed all 218 projects. Of these, 154 were in eight combinations. The remaining 64 projects were discarded. Regional tabulations revealed relationships between region and certain community types. Other arbitrary criteria dictated that the municipality serving as the site for the hospital be a county seat, and that the sites be free of major related institutions, i. e., large colleges and universities, state hospitals, and penal institutions.

The Northeast region is illustrative of case selection. Twenty-four Hill-Burton projects, meeting the general criteria for the study, returned questionnaires. Eighteen of the 24 projects were those with a relatively low need for a hospital, low rurality, high population in the service area, and a relatively large goal as measured by the number of hospital beds. For the 18 projects, 16 had employed professional fund-raisers. Three of the 16 were in county seat towns. One project was selected in western New York state with the application of such judgment factors as distance and accessibility.

In this way, five projects were selected for intensive investigation. They were in the states of New York, Indiana, Alabama, Wyoming, and California. The Southwest region was eliminated. This was done because the cooperative hospitals in this region appeared different than the usual Hill-Burton projects and, too, other workers had specifically studied them in detail.[4] Thus, a wise use of funds made the study of a single case in the Southwest appear impractical for the purposes of the present study.

Field work began with the Indiana project, hereafter termed the Midstate case. This beginning was exploratory with Midstate serving as the setting for a reconnaissance seminar attended by members of the project committee and consultants. Reviewing records and interviewing by day, with committee sessions by night, stimulated theory and method in its development from first form to readiness for the field. Even the second study in Wyoming, hereafter termed Norwest, was partly exploratory. After the Indiana experience, research teams composed of three or four workers proceeded to the New York case (Noreast), then to California (Farwest), and finally to Alabama (Southeast). No two teams were staffed by identical personnel, yet it was planned that two staff members serve alternately as leaders.

Each field trip was given particular preparation. After contacting official agents of the respective hospital project to gain approval for the study, arrival dates and work and living accommodations were arranged. Individual team members assembled and reviewed the socioeconomic data for the service hospital area, its history, the proximity to metropolitan centers, and the materials previously obtained from the questionnaire and other sources. The briefing went one step further to include a series of training meetings for the team members. It was here that theory and method were discussed, especially the experiences in preceding studies. Expectations regarding the forthcoming case were studied. Special features of the project, as provided by the questionnaire responses, were noted. Although adaptations in field methods were discussed, training sessions stressed the essential need for insuring the comparability of the five case studies.

Once in the field, an average of 13 days was spent on each case by the research team. After appropriate identification and introduction of team members, five core procedures were initiated. The first was that of reconstructing the detailed sequence of events for the respective project. To accomplish this purpose, a thorough examination of local newspapers was made to note events, persons, plans, dates, and relevant items about both the hospital project and the community's social organization. This investigation yielded a reconstructed chronology of events. The second step was to submit the statement to members of the concerned hospital board for full discussion and eventual redrafting.

The third step was to complete a schedule of questions, answers to which might reflect the general community setting in which the project was completed. This information included the beliefs of informants about already existing hospital facilities, their attitudes toward the manner in which the local project was completed, and their recommendations to other communities attempting a similar task. Of essential importance was the need to gain images held by community residents of hospital project leaders and the roles which they played. The names of leaders were selected on the basis of frequency and intensity of participation and placed on the interview schedule as an aid to gaining a community image of the basis of their leadership.

The schedule was administered to four categories of informants: members of the hospital board, leaders of the fund-raising campaign, selected rural leaders, and the formal officers of relevant community associations. Accordingly, the schedule was administered to some 40 informants in each case.

A fourth field procedure was a series of intensive interviews with the centrally important participants. The interviews were developed around a previously prepared schematic diagram of the dynamics of the project. Each important participant, with reference to the schematic diagram, was then encouraged to describe the form and content of negotiations he had pursued with others, and his relationships and images thereof with other participants in the project. This procedure provided depth for the understanding of what had happened in the community, especially from the vantage point of the "inner circles" of participating persons.

A fifth and final field procedure was the mailing of a postal card questionnaire to a sample of the registered voters in the hospital service community. The purpose was to obtain some measure of the awareness of the mass of community residents which had not directly participated. Of special interest was their placing of credit for the efforts of others, together with an estimation of public sentiment as to the need for a hospital.

In addition, systematic note-taking was practiced in the field, and initial analyses and descriptive profiles were developed. These were completed, after the return of the research team, in a series of seminars conducted by the project committee.

Even a minimum outline of procedure will suggest the organization of a research report. The evolution of a research project inevitably puts its stamp on the report. With the foregoing narrative, a preview has been given of the core interests for the study: (1) an emphasis on hospital development with health department and prepayment plan organizations providing supplementary comparisons; (2) a concern with regional contrasts in community action toward major health goals; (3) an attempted complementary use of two methods in social research, the mailed questionnaire and the case study; and (4) a stress upon the flow and the essential characteristics of community action as shown by the questionnaire material, and an illumination of some subtleties of community action by the case method of study.

I. PERSPECTIVE

THIS IS a book about an idea—that health is, in part, an enterprise of the community. Too, this is a book about a process—that of employing community resources for gains in good health. It presents a view of small communities in a quest for major health goals—a hospital, a local health department, a consumer plan of paying for medical care. This is not a book about hospitals alone, or only of health departments or prepayment plans. Yet efforts toward these goals have produced reverberations in American communities, and it is these reverberations that are of present interest. This book, then, becomes a story essentially more about the community than about health.

Social scientists look upon the community as one point of scholarly inquiry. In the phenomenon known as "public health", they see a promise for the labors of research. Both are true here. Well-known in the literature of social science are a sociology of mental health,[1] a measurement of health and medical need[2] and of the usage of health facilities.[3] One encounters an ecology of medical service,[4] sociological views of morbidity and mortality,[5] and sociological studies of health as a social movement,[6] of public opinion in health affairs,[7] and of medical practice as a pattern of human relationships.[8] All these are worthy in their own right, but here the present essential interest is to contribute solely to an understanding of small communities as they accept major challenges in the field of health.

Choosing a Focus

THERE are possible multiple perspectives for scholarly inquiry of the community. Each demands some definition, especially what is meant by the idea of community. Throughout the present effort, the community is viewed as a localized group which relates to an identifiable, geographical area, and focuses in one or more patterns of services, communication, and formal and informal controls of human conduct. The specific nature of this study further encourages a treatment of the community as a geographical area including those persons with an interest in, with an anticipation for, or who receive, the services of a major health facility.[9]

In scope, the present work focuses on those parts of the total community which appear to some degree operative in community problem-solving. The city and country, although parts of the same community, may fail to be one in health affairs. The factors of age, sex, kinship, occupation, and friendship may make a difference in participation. Few communities are any longer distinct and isolated. Countless health programs have wide areas of support and administration, on national, regional, and state levels. Designing health services for the urbanized Northeast is different from planning for the sparsely populated Great Plains. Finally, the contrasts of community life in a complex industrial society, with its delegation to specialized agencies of the burden of action on problems of health, encourages an inquiry into all such agencies—voluntary, service, business, and fraternal—which influence health programs both at the rural crossroads and in the metropolitan centers of the land.[10]

There are several avenues to community inquiry. One avenue leads to a description of the major cultural features of the community—its habits and customs, its technology, its beliefs and values, and its organization. These studies are amply descriptive, but they minimize basic comparisons. They deal instead with the totality of cultural features within a community—as did the classic studies of the Lynds—and frequently concern adjustments in the totality resulting from the impact of changing social and economic conditions.[11]

Another scholarly avenue encourages intensive investigation of selected features of community life. Examples are the studies of Warner and his colleagues, which deal with the community in terms of clique, associational, and social class behavior.[12] A frequent additional concern of these works is with race relations. This may be noted in the studies of Powdermaker, Davis and Gardner, Drake and Cayton, and Dollard.[13] All of these efforts place an emphasis on social relationships in their involvements with social status and caste distinctions.

A third avenue of inquiry is frequently chosen by the rural sociologists, that of investigating community stability and instability. These studies often portray the consequences to community stability of changing features of the community—population, economics, group life, and social visiting patterns. One example is that of the Rural Life Studies of the Bureau of Agricultural Economics of the U. S. Department of Agriculture.[14] Finally, the most casual student of the community is familiar with that large group of studies dealing with the rules and methods of stimulating, organizing, and allocating community resources toward some desirable objective. Although these presentations build up on considerable factual information, they usually do not follow after rigorous experimentation and investigation. Examples include Morgan's treatment of the small community, the Virginia activities summarized by the Ogdens, and the compilation of reports by Sanders.[15]

An examination of scholarly endeavors in the community field suggests certain needs for additional community inquiry. One need is for a greater comparative understanding of community activity, in a variety of situations, toward a concrete and identical goal. In this instance, dealing with all the problems and goals involved in a single community makes for difficulty in planning a comparative approach. A second need results from the frequent necessity of considering only an individual community or, at best, a small number. This condition, too, retards quantitative investigations of community action in a variety of situations. A third need concerns the connection between the community and the larger society—the state, the region, and the nation as a whole. The present study assumes that few communities are any longer confined to their own limits for the stimulation, mobilization, and organization of local resources. Indeed, agencies on many levels of administration provide a vast network of communication in which conmunities, large and small, are involved.[16]

Detailed Perspectives

COMMUNITY action toward a goal may, first of all, be viewed as a sequence of happenings. The mobilization of community resources proceeds by stages, through time, to either success or failure. This sequence of events or happenings must be classified in any thorough community investigation. The present study makes such a classification, with four stages of community action deemed essential. The first is *prior community situation,* dealing with the early and often particular circumstances of community need.[17] For major health facilities one finds included such situational factors as the extent of financial resources, community crisis, legislative restrictions, and the delays and oppositions preceding community action. The second stage is the *initiation of action.* It is concerned with individual or group initiation, gaining approval for the original idea, and meeting the problems of getting under way. A third stage is the *organization of sponsorship.* This includes both the primary groups that assume official sponsorship and the secondary groups that provide specific community resources. A fourth stage is that of *community organization methods,* or the techniques by which resources are mobilized, such as the use of communication media and other types of appeals made to the community. These four stages are segments along the time schedule of community action. They will be guideposts in organizing and describing the major events in small community efforts toward major health goals.

Acquiring modern health facilities is a most important goal to the community which sets its course toward them. This is usually true in the small community. Given people and leaders, needs and resources, the health facility is not acquired until someone or some group acts. To act is to decide. Resulting community decisions channel the efforts of the people, limit them to specific courses of action, and prescribe certain community efforts. Because of this, all the residents in a community do not make the decisions. The public-at-large may suggest the need for decision and action, and eventually the people must render approval and share in the consequences. Yet not all take part in the same way.[18] These differences in participation in the making of decisions are of special interest in this study. The making of decisions, securing of approval for them, and carrying them out, are termed, in combination, the decision-making process.

The Decision-Making Process

A DECISION serves to reduce the number of alternative courses of action available to persons or groups in community action toward major health goals. The hospital, the local health department, the consumer-sponsored prepayment plan for medical care—all result after specific procedures are carried out. Sifting the possible procedures to the point that people agree to accept and engage in directed community activity is a result of decisions made.[19] Still, a decision to reduce the alternative courses of action is of no consequence unless it appears "rightful" to those for whom the decision applies. The appearance of "rightfulness" renders the decision *legitimate*. Hence, legitimacy refers to the rights of some persons to make decisions, and draws on certain capacities of "rightfulness" possessed by the decision-maker.[20] These capacities may be said to be "built into" some positions and offices within the community, so that the incumbents possess the right to make local decisions for acquiring major health facilities. Such capacities are of special interest in this study.

However, "rightfulness" or legitimacy for decision-making purposes may not be associated entirely with certain community positions and offices. It is then that *approval* may become important. Approval may be given by certain community groups, by some persons, or by all the people, i. e., by referendum. Even the approval of some one person or group may be necessary for certain decisions while, at other times, the approval of all the people may be required. When correct approval is secured, the decision appears "rightful" to those to whom the decision applies.

> In one hospital project two members of the local hospital board—for an already operating hospital—decided that the employment of a professional fund-raiser was necessary to solve the problem of adequate construction funds. The two members arranged for the fund-raiser to visit the community secretly and to estimate financial resources without the knowledge of other board members and other persons in the community. The professional fund-raiser finally appeared before the hospital board which officially approved his employment. In this way, two board members made a decision, the hospital board gave approval, and—as community informants indicated—the decision became legitimate to the entire community: "The hospital board knows best about the hospital situation, and it was their responsibility to do something about it."

Finally, decisions are of no consequence if they fail to be carried out. *Decision-execution* is a matter of community participation and of administration. Primarily, the carrying out of activities for which decisions provide brings with it the tasks of mobilizing, allocating, and manipulating the social and economic resources of the community. One intent of decision-making for major health goals always is to gain approval or consensus of community organizations and, frequently, of the total community. But unintended consequences may result and produce opposition to deter the progress of the project.[21]

> For the hospital project cited in the above illustration, the professional fund-raiser was employed. To carry out this decision brought an extensive and complex community arrangement to raise funds involving town and country alike, as well as the majority of organized groups in the community.

Decision-Making Capacities

AN understanding of community action toward any community goal depends on an identification not only of those who make the decisions, but also of the way in which the maker acquires the "rightfulness" to make them legitimately. For the present purpose, the two major capacities of "rightful" decision-making are considered to be authority and influence.[22] Decisions are made when the capacity of authority is possessed, or when the capacity of influence is possessed, or through combinations of both.

The capacity of authority is that body of rights and privileges belonging to certain roles within the community. Of greatest importance in the present study is that of *office*.[23] Office refers to the separation of the members-at-large of an organization and the positions of leadership within it which express the collective aims of the total group. Thus, authority results from an awareness of the members-at-large and the officer-holder, alike, that when the latter issues an order the collective interests of the organization are being served. *Family* position within the community, the prestige of a particular *kinship* group, or even socio-economic *status*—all these may contribute additionally to a measure of authority based on position.[24]

The capacity of influence is primarily that collection of relevant resources and proficiencies which the maker of decisions brings to the community action project. The degree of possession of resources and proficiencies must be deemed essential to the task at hand, or such possession may not provide the capacity of influence. The following illustrations will define the manner in which influence undergirds the making of decisions in a "rightful" way.

The successful completion of a major health facility usually demands extensive finances. This may require an extensive mobilization of community wealth. The person who commits the community to a financial task must accept the responsibility of behaving in accordance with the decision that commits others. In this way, the possessor of influence—as it is found in community health projects—may find a personal resource of *wealth* an appropriate ingredient of influence.[25]

> In one hospital project one of the prominent leaders provided the largest personal contribution in a fund-raising drive. As reported, he promised to double the amount in the event of insufficient funds. Community informants reported: "He is the sort of fellow who won't go after the other fellow's dollar without giving one himself." "He has lots of money and would argue over $.25 on the matter of principle, but wouldn't haggle over $2,500 for a just community cause." "Whenever he goes to a church supper, you can expect a five dollar bill under the plate when it is over."

One of the deference values in every community is that of *respect*.[26] This is an intrinsic valuation of the person, and largely refers to his actual or imagined standing in the estimation of other persons. These estimations not only provide one ranking of community residents, but add another resource for the "rightful" making of decisions affecting the community. That this is true of community endeavors for major health goals is indicated by the following references.

> In one hospital project a prominent county-wide leader, who was centrally active, was credited with respect by such revealing comments as: "Everybody likes him and it isn't because he is wealthy; it's the way he acts. He greets you on the street as he does in his own place of business." "He's a good one and his brother is the same." "They got plenty but they give a world of stuff away."

15

In the same project another prominent hospital leader was credited with such contrasting comments as: "He will work hard but he wants his name in the paper." "He'll carry things through but won't play unless he can be the boss." "He's too self-confident—always wanting to run everything and not give and take." "Around here when you get to be somebody you can spoil it by acting too much like it. That's his trouble."

Some persons in the community become, as it were, the symbols of the values held by the community as to what is morally correct. This condition provides for the resources of *morality*, or the community impression that "they can do no wrong." Respect deals with the valuations of the person, morality deals with the valuations of what he stands for.[27]

The following statements were made about one leading person in a hospital project: "He is the personification of the community." "When he got in it I knew that nothing could prevent its (the hospital) success." "He works with a pretty fast crowd, but he knows what to take of it and what to leave alone."

The resource of *success* refers to a community viewpoint that some persons always meet with success in public ventures. It is then a matter of community expectation that whatever such a person may pursue is bound to succeed and not to fail. These expectations form a resource which the decision-maker of influence may bring to the community action project.[28]

In one hospital project, representative informants commented about the leading worker in the project: "He never failed at anything he ever started." "He put his church on its feet and a lot of other things, too." "He gets things done that he starts; he's really a doer."

Active participants in community action toward community goals frequently possess extensive acquaintanceship with groups and individuals within and without the community. The possession of *access* means that the participant has opportunities to be a part of, or be able to contact, important individuals and groups both within the community and, if necessary, those on higher levels of relevant concern to the community project. Access may range from "knowing everyone in the community," through membership in prestiged groups, and up to state, regional, and national connections.[29]

In all of the hospital projects intensively studied, one or more of the leaders had access to persons and organizations on state levels. In each project, leaders could gain the attention of locally important associations and clubs. In one case informants ranked a local service club, a male athletic club, and the directors of a local business as centrally important groups in town. The four centrally important leaders of the hospital project held joint membership in each and all of them. As these men were spoken of, "they know everyone in the whole county," and "their business contacts are spread over the state."

Another resource of influence is that of *obligation*.[30] Every community resident is, of course, involved in a set of reciprocal relationships and, hence, reciprocal obligations. Obligation refers to a value of "being in one's debt until it is repaid." Thus, the individual, through acts of goodwill, helping, and friendliness, deposits in the community a measure of obligation to him, which may be recalled when needed.

> One prominent leader in a hospital project was reported by every community informant to have helped practically everyone in the community. The following comments are illustrative: "During a serious illness of a member of my family, he visited almost every day for five years after the community had forgotten it. This is the kind of thing that makes you stick with him." "He always has a benefit ticket in his pocket—scouts, church, or something. He's always trying to help the worth-while things of the community."

Community action necessarily demands the expenditure of *time* on the part of its leaders. Although other resources of influence are available, the lack of time to participate in the activity may remove one from the details of community decision-making. That the community-at-large may recognize this is indicated by the following illustration.

> "He played a big part. He was able to give it more time than any man in the community. You have to find this kind of man, with time or money, when you are selecting local men to head up a campaign." "He not only has ability, but the time to spend on community activities." "He was so active it wasn't even funny. He came through snowstorms to get to meetings—walking, too."

As the preceding illustrations suggest, the resources of influence for those engaging in community pursuits of major health goals have to do with the historical doings of the individual with his fellows. Of great importance are the valuations which the community-at-large places upon them. For the purposes of achieving major health goals in the community, however, influence may depend on the particular proficiencies of active participants. Of primary importance is *subject matter competence*, which refers to the knowledge possessed of the field of consideration.[31]

> In one hospital project the leading person had maintained an interest in hospitals over a period of time, possessed an extensive library on the subject, and attended frequent professional conferences devoted to hospital construction and maintenance. The following comments are illustrative: "I relied a great deal on his knowledge of hospitals." "He has been looking at hospitals for several years." "He always wants to know the facts, and always studies things out."

Community action is, by definition, a problem of organization. Hence, specific proficiencies of participants in the way of *organizational skills* enter not only into effective decision-making but are usually deemed essential.[32]

> The professional fund-raiser in one hospital project was credited with immediate influence due to the possession of organizational skill. "He was the maestro of the concert. . . . I can see him now! He had a definite plan to raise money. He explained the need for a hospital, involved others who knew the need, and got them to serve on committees." "He put everything in proper relation and set the spark . . . tied it all together and set it going." "He really knew what he was doing . . . never heard a person who could say so many words in five minutes, not what 'I' can do, but what the 'community' could do."

Another proficiency is the ability to know and to manipulate appropriate community symbols. Achieving a major health goal, such as the hospital, depends on effecting proper appeals to the community, justifying fund-raising plans, and communicating arguments for the new facility to the community. That *skill with symbols* is not forgotten by the community-at-large is indicated by the illustrative comments given in one hospital project.[33]

> "I can hardly believe that it happened to us—we were caught in the midst of a great revival meeting." "I'll never forget how we used to sing before we started our campaign meetings." "As I look back at it now, I was so much in favor of the hospital that if I had been pressed I would have deeded over my house to them (the leaders, among them a professional fund-raiser).

In addition to the possession of the resources and proficiencies cited above, some persons in the community may be so venerated that their personalities and exploits become legend. Thus, eccentric features of personality may be so legendary in the community that they are symbolic of the presence or lack of influence. This ingredient may be termed the *legendary personality*.[34]

> In one hospital project a prominent leader was frequently commented about as follows: "When he begins to get nervous, look out—something is about to happen in the community." "He has the most nervous energy of anyone I ever saw. When he is at the club he is running madly between the card table, the rest room, and the pool table." "One time he helped arbitrate a local strike. After a day of dealing with him the union leader remarked, 'He's the damndest fellow I was ever up against.' "

> In the same project, another leader was held to have the legend feature of vigor. One legend tale involved a nine-mile walk through driving snow to attend a meeting of which he was chairman. As one informant put it, "You can imagine the effect it had on us all, who had decided that he could not possibly make it, when he walked in with his snowshoes over his shoulder."

Decision-Making Operations

COMMUNITY action viewed as a decision-making process requires an understanding of the necessary decisions, of those who make them, of the capacities of "rightfulness," and of how the capacities are organized in the community so that some possess them and participate in decision-making, and some do not. In one sense, decision-making in community organization is a deployment of related capacities in order to reach an intended goal. The major operation by which the deployment occurs is that of *strategy*, which is a plan to acquire or neutralize those resources and proficiencies possessed by others than the active participants in the community activity. The possession of decision-making capacities by others may mean the threat of opposition. To contain the opposition is essentially a problem of acquiring or neutralizing the unpossessed capacities.

> In one hospital project the initiating leaders happened to be excluded from the large landowners of the county, a prevailing group which not only controlled

the votes of the county but also possessed extensive influence in county affairs. The initiators of the project immediately recognized that the influence of the landowners had to be either acquired or neutralized. The resulting strategy was that of getting the landowners committed in the public eye, thus making them appear as a part of the sponsoring group.

Frequently a plan of strategy includes a number of steps to accomplish its purposes. *Tactics* are the active and coherent steps which lead to the fulfillment of strategy. In the quest for major health goals, both strategy and tactics are accomplished largely through *negotiations*. One pattern of negotiation is direct, the decision-makers consult with each other; another is indirect, or other intermediary persons and groups are employed.

In the foregoing illustration, the strategy of securing the large landowners of the county as partial sponsors of the hospital project included two tactics: (1) negotiating with the County Commissioners Court to have the landowners appointed to a "hospital committee;" and (2) the composition of the committee was published in the newspaper. As one large landowner stated: "When I saw my name in the paper I knew then that they had me. After all, I could hardly be against an obviously good thing like a hospital."

The Purpose

THE presentation to follow is a study of contrast. The guiding purposes are actually threefold: (1) to demonstrate the over-all similarities and dissimilarities in the community action plans for acquiring hospitals, local health departments, and consumer-sponsored prepayment plans; (2) to portray some of the subtleties of decision-making in community action in various sections of the United States, by employing a sixfold regional classification of hospital projects; and (3) to reflect some phases of problem, of method, of planning, and of cooperation as the citizens of small communities turn to the improvement of health facilities.

Although this book is a report of research, it also aims to interpret moderately some aspects of small-town America. The rigors of research cannot veil the anxieties and the cooperation of the people along Main Street. Back of every health project employed in this study there stands enthusiasm, disappointment, anger, faith in achievement, the time and the sweat and the worry of small-town Americans in perfecting what they consider a better place in which to live.

II. BEDS, BRICKS, AND PEOPLE

THIS IS a story of 218 successful community efforts to acquire hospitals. It is essentially an account of courts and bond issues, Main Street business, street corner discussion, agreement and conflict, election and debate, memorials and architects. The story cannot possibly capture the drama in this hospital quest of everyday citizens. Yet, this over-view shows a pattern of local activity which is distinctively expressive of small-town America.

Early Community Situations [1]

THE birth of the hospital idea as an actively-sought goal occurred in each community when there was a certain "readiness" shown by public attitudes of hospital need, of crisis, and of past experience in community endeavor. Present, too, were awareness of the expense of acquiring a hospital, the need of funds, and the prospects of raising them. Compliance with provisions of Hill-Burton legislation found some communities high in desire but low in priority, others the reverse. Whatever the community situation, considerable discussion occurred before definite action was under way. Eight in ten projects reported a "long and gradual period of development," and nine in ten spent two to ten years between first interest and initial action.

The time-lapse is readily explained by the two-thirds of the communities which credited "insufficient funds" as delaying an active project. More than half of the communities gave credit to financial support from federal sources for removing such delays. In addition, the advent of World War II impeded many plans already under way, indicating that small community activity for better health was smoldering early in the "forties." The end of the war and an immediate upswing in community health discussion prepared the way for approaching Hill-Burton legislation.

Peculiar and individual factors frequently characterized community situations early in their health progress. Case studies provided an opportunity to view some of these factors. In two of the projects, people had worried increasingly over departing physicians. In one community the exodus left none. Both communities were aware that one important reason for these departures was the local lack of modern hospital facilities, and the resulting desire of physicians to further their medical careers elsewhere. In two other projects treated as case studies, dissatisfaction developed with privately-operated hospitals. In one community, citizens became suspicious of the caliber of hospital practice. Two leading residents, after visiting a friend in the private hospital, observed what they believed to be inadequate patient care. They reacted by removing the friend from the local hospital to a larger facility some 40 miles distant. These persons later became the initial apostles for a new community hospital.

In the fifth case, people began to rumor about the physical conditions of the existing hospital—a converted dwelling. One person said, "Going to the hospital was like spending some time in the refrigerator. They could mend your leg but you might have pneumonia when you were discharged." Another person exclaimed, "The old hospital had become so crowded that I heard they were using bathtubs for beds." And as another put it, "When I was at the hospital recently, I spent most of my time attempting to dodge the water that was dripping from the roof." Rumors had circulated the length of Main Street about the resident who, after suffering an accident, was unable to gain space in the local hospital. He was taken to another, but eventually died.

Added to such occurrences, often interpreted as crises in many communities, was the impact of increasing health education sponsored by educational institutions, state hospital associations and, in some areas, health foundations.[2] Also, examination of each community situation revealed many residents engaged in programs of health in farm organizations, civic and fraternal clubs, parent-teacher groups, women's clubs, and many community associations.

Initiation of Action

IMPORTANT to the present review was the delineation of the initiators of action, especially the form taken by the initiation. In 32 percent of the 218 projects, one person was credited with actively initiating a concrete plan. For 28 percent, credit was given to "several persons working together." In 12 percent, an organized group was looked back upon as the primary initiator of the new hospital idea. The remainder reported some combination of individuals and organized groups. Business and industries rarely served in initiating roles, only two percent of the projects so reporting.

Once having initiated the project, the same persons usually continued to share major responsibilities. To identify them in the organization of the community, a survey of occupation held was deemed appropriate.[T-2] From the findings of the study, the task of new hospital development in small communities was shown to be primarily a masculine enterprise.[3] Among 670 persons termed "most active" by the reporting projects, only a negligible number were women. Further, the enterprise was a task for those occupations oriented to business in village, town, and city. As a reference to Figure 1 will indicate, the occupation appearing most often was that of self-employed businessman, followed by professional and employed manager or executive. Activity was keenest along Main Street, with two-thirds of the active participants either businessmen, professionals, or executives. Farm people provided "most active" persons to the extent of ten percent. Only four percent of the "most active" group were non-supervisory employees. Finally, it was a self-employed businessman who frequently occurred two or more times within any one set of four most active persons. In 15 percent of the projects, two self-employed businessmen were members of the four highest-ranked participants in each instance.

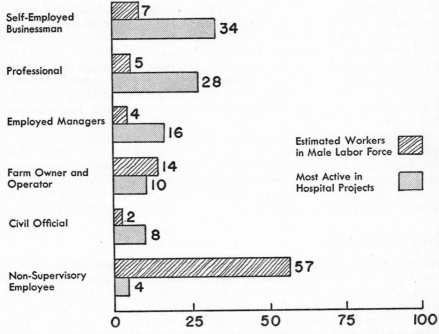

FIGURE 1. Percentage Incidence of Occupational Position of Persons Named Most Active in 218 Hospital Projects

Official Sponsorship

EVERY community action plan provided for a sponsoring group. Not only did the Hill-Burton projects require an official sponsor, but many community needs were served by the existence of an official group ever vigilant in matters of keeping the community-at-large informed, in securing approval for particular practices, in sensing potential opposition to community plans, and in reducing the amount of opposition if necessary.

The 218 successfully completed projects were most frequently sponsored by existing or newly-formed hospital boards or associations. In six out of ten projects, a formal board or association presided officially over the community plan. At times, the hospital board for an already-existing hospital continued as the sponsor for the new one. In other instances, the hospital board was formed immediately after initiation of the project, but prior to the construction of the hospital. County or municipal governing bodies provided official sponsorship in two out of ten projects. County governing bodies, i. e., Commissioners Courts and Boards of Supervisors, were more active than municipal bodies. Indeed, almost half of the 218 projects were based on the jurisdictional unit of the county. Accordingly, county government would be expected to play an integral part in planning. One in five projects was sponsored by community-wide citizens' councils, and three percent by health councils.[4] Very few reports were made of farm organizations, churches, councils of social agencies, and women's clubs as central sponsors.[T-3]

Community sponsorship involved more than the centrally important sponsoring group. Many community and county-wide associations provided the project with various physical, human, and financial resources. Civic and service clubs usually were active supporters, specifically, Chambers of Commerce, Lions, Kiwanis, Rotary, American Legion, Veterans of Foreign Wars, and the Farm Bureau.[5] In ranking the incidence of participation for these service clubs, the Chamber of Commerce, Lions, and Rotary groups occupied the top three positions. This evidence supports the conclusion that the town or city site for the hospital must be considered a most important subgrouping in community decision-making.

Certain practices of sponsorship provide a cue for the way in which the usual sponsoring group went about its task. For instance, the number of members of official sponsoring groups was relatively low, especially in specifically formed hospital boards and associations. Extensive arrangements such as subcommittees and budgets were of slight importance. Only 12 percent of the official sponsoring groups maintained a working budget, and but 20 percent found it necessary to appoint subcommittees to assume detailed responsibilities. In addition, the majority of the projects reported no paid assistance in community hospital planning.[T-4]

Sponsorship is a process in itself. An early problem, as reported by the 218 projects, was how to transfer community residents to positions of sponsoring responsibility. The chosen practice expresses, in part, the style of attack which the community makes on local problems. For the 218 projects two methods of member selection were favored: appointment by local officials, and community elections. Less frequent was the appointment of members by community associations, a device often employed in traditional plans of community organization. With sponsoring groups primarily taking the form of hospital boards and local governing bodies, it is not surprising that direct appointment by civil officials and community-wide elections would be selected as appropriate methods.[T-5]

Central sponsoring groups were organized, for the most part, for the particular task of acquiring a hospital. Two out of three sponsoring groups had never before served in a similar capacity in previous community activities. The evidence suggests that the magnitude of the hospital project in the eyes of the community-at-large led to organizing sponsorship for a specific task. The hospital project was interpreted largely as a problem in finance, tending to call forth, as previous comments indicate, those individuals and associations with skills related to the management of community funds.

The Problems of Sponsorship [6]

THE paths to the 218 successful hospital projects did not escape a variety of obstacles. Among the many problems reported, it is notable that those dealing with "disagreements between members" of the sponsoring groups were lacking. In a few cases, professional and lay members reached points of disagreement, especially in regard to site planning and architectural design. Professionals and lay persons, too, occasionally differed on the method of raising funds. Surprising, indeed, are the reports that more than half of the projects met only positive feelings and relationships between members of the official group. This equanimity was undoubtedly a factor in the success of the projects. As a solution for such internal problems, one hospital project reported: ". . . our promotional firm, plus the diplomacy of local trustees, managed to avoid most of the unpleasant experiences." In several such instances, professional fund-raisers were credited with preventing and solving interpersonal differences.

One project reported that a major internal problem was ". . . the hospital manager under the old regime, but we finally solved the problem by discharging him." Other reports implied that certain members of sponsoring groups ". . . failed to complete personal assignments." Several projects indicated that ". . . a small group that wanted a hospital for their own town caused considerable trouble between members of the board." Another report was this: ". . . we had a little difficulty in getting local doctors to agree on size and plans but this was not serious."

One reported concern was the great difference in time and energy given to the project by various members of the sponsoring body. As it was put in one project, "Only two members of the board seemed willing to put forth the required effort, while the other three members seemed willing to have them do so." Another reporter stated, "The two individuals who conceived the idea of a hospital and stayed with it until it was accomplished . . . explored every possibility before they met with final success. . . . [They] engineered a successful municipal election to form a hospital district."

One universal area of potential difficulty was the maintenance of communication between the official sponsoring group and the community-at-large. In some stages of activity, the greatest problems confronting the sponsoring body concerned subgroupings of the community, i. e., other towns and villages within the service area. Continually present was the opportunity for conflict between different parts of the community. The rivalry between two towns or cities, appearing on the surface as athletic competition, frequently flared into conflict over the location of the hospital. Forty percent of the reporting projects had met and solved conflicts between neighboring towns or counties, and 25 percent reported resistance from outlying areas of the community. It was commonly explained that local residents living on the perimeter of the proposed service area were frequently closer to another hospital. Hence, they were undecided in their interests, loyalties, and promised future use of the new facility.

24

Site Problems

THE following quotations from the reports are indicative of location difficulty: "Jealousy and rivalry between towns". . . . "Misrepresentation of facts by newspapers in towns jealous of the county seat where the hospital was proposed". . . . "Some persons offered to donate the site and this had the effect of politics getting into the program". . . . "First we tried to have a county hospital voted, as our city is the county seat, but a larger city in the county which had a hospital (church-controlled) turned out en masse and voted it down. We forgot the county hospital idea and worked on a community project and a local election for the above issued carried". . . ."We got mixed in county politics with every town in the county wanting to get the hospital". . . . "Other towns have always been jealous of our county seat". . . . "There was a reluctance of persons in towns or cities in the hospital area to make financial contributions on account of the hospital not being planned for their own city". . . . "We had considerable opposition about the location which was purchased and donated by our own Chamber of Commerce."

Justifying the hospital to the community, a question of need, was a persistent problem for the sponsoring groups. As found in Figure 2, in 48 percent of the reporting projects, an insufficient feeling of need on the part of the people became active resistance at some stage of the development. As one project report stated, "We were always struggling with statements about the fact that the hospital was unnecessary."

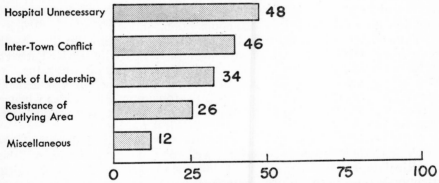

FIGURE 2. Percentage Incidence of Major Problems Encountered by Sponsoring Groups of 218 Hospital Projects

About 60 percent of those reporting on projects believed that certain problems with particular groups and individuals impeded an orderly development. First among these were problems of resistance from influential persons in the area. Such resistance was commonly motivated by explicit arguments concerning the necessity for a new hospital, concerns over location, and not infrequently by political alignments. As one report included, ". . . . one member of the city commission joined with a group of influential citizens to oppose the building of a new hospital and the location of same, and tried to block it by bringing a lawsuit to stop the sale of bonds." Other reports included: "One banker attempted to block, but promotion was carefully enough planned that opposition could not develop followers—so they joined, or resisted, in silence." . . . . "Opposition came from economically-minded citizens who questioned the possibility of accomplishing the project." . . . . "the usual few who are professional 'against-ers'" . . . . "Some influential citizens felt it would cause the privately owned hospital to close and bring financial ruin to the one doctor in the community." Several reports indicated apathy on the part of influential citizens, as . . . . "some were satisfied with conditions as they were" . . . . "lack of understanding" . . . . "social inertia" . . . . "competition between influential church leaders."

Conflicting Pressures

THE following quotations from a variety of project reports indicate some of the problems with influential persons and groups: "Some difference of opinion on who should operate the hospital, Catholic or Protestant" . . . . "The County Commissioners were cool toward the project at first" . . . . "A few wanted to convert the local county home into a hospital rather than a new building" . . . . "Jealousy and lack of harmony between doctors" . . . . "A few prominent citizens argued that it would be only a nice set-up for the doctors" . . . . "That the hospital was a good idea but the doctors should pay for it" . . . . "One man trying to do the whole job was disliked by a great many people of influence" . . . . "Ministers of churches, which were building new churches, put a cold shoulder to the competition for donations" . . . . "We had a few merchants who fought the hospital because they thought they would not gain financially" . . . . "Some prominent people gave lip service but were really out against the hospital" . . . . "A few outstanding citizens refused to have any interest until they saw that hospital construction was actually started" . . . . "Some of the top leaders in the town opposed the idea when an outsider was hired to help raise money" . . . . "Some very good people feared that the hospital would be just another political football."

An over-view of problems met by the 218 projects indicates that a perplexing problem was the successful weighting of representatives of other municipalities and counties within the hospital service area. Frequently, little attention was given to uniform representation when sponsoring groups were formed. Hence, all members might be recruited from the city and none from the rural hinterlands. In other instances, the reverse was true. The old problem of intellegent representation still persists to challenge early efforts of community improvement projects. As one report stated: "Sponsoring groups must not be too closely tied to one institution or clique within the community. It is important that they have both lay and professional leadership, and that they reach the masses as well as the privileged few." Several reports testified to the difficult task of forming the "perfect" sponsoring group, for . . . . "we often find that a group is zealous but with very little influence in terms of the power structure in the community." The answer to this error, as frequently reported, is to permit such a sponsoring group to do the "spade work" but quickly to get an established organization of influence actively engaged.

Of all the problems encountered, the previously mentioned resistance to the financial magnitude of the hospital project was most troublesome. Community fears over higher taxes were associated with project after project. In five of ten projects, active opposition to threatened high taxes was encountered.[T-6] Yet, as many reports explained, the use of high taxes as a central argument was often a masquerade for other deeply felt reasons. As an example, in one case study the opposition of old and traditional families, although publicly based on the "tax" argument, resulted from fears by such families that they could no longer compete in giving with more wealthy newcomers to the community.

Organizational Methods

THE presence of need, the formation of sponsorship, and the meeting of early opposition—all determined the community setting in which the toil of raising money and initiating construction occurred. In addition, success in gaining the hospital goal depended on an ability to translate the general striving for a hospital into specific goals of raising money in a campaign, negotiating with local governing bodies, and developing educational programs for the community. No hospital cornerstone was placed until weeks and months of planning was accomplished.

A necessary decision early in the hospital project was the choice of a fund-raising method. Although Hill-Burton provisions added federal aid to construction costs, the community was left with the rest, varying from one-third to one-half the total cost. The choice made established the style of community organization to follow. This all depended on whether the community obtained the services of a professional, employed a voluntary drive with local leadership, or approached civil bodies for formal appropriations.

About half of the 218 projects selected voluntary gift campaigns under local direction, and almost half elected the county bond issue to gain public approval for county appropriations. Seventeen percent of the projects invited a professional fund-raiser to develop and direct a voluntary gift campaign. In some instances, combinations of the three basic campaign types were believed necessary. Other types of fund-raising devices, employed less often, included the municipal bond issue, cooperative memberships, and the "hospital district" device of the Far West, actually an incorporation of the hospital service area for the legal purpose of building and maintaining hospital facilities.[7] Thirty-three projects in the Far West states made this selection.[T-7]

After the fund-raising method or methods were chosen the organization and conduct of a community campaign became the most intense event in the hospital construction plan. A common method employed by the 218 projects was that of focusing the campaign in a short period of time. The general recommendation of the projects was to stress but one to three months as the optimum time-span of the fund-raising period. In two out of ten projects, the campaign was less than two weeks in duration; in four out of ten projects the time-span was less than two months; and only one project in ten utilized a period as long as a year.

Raising sufficient funds for hospital construction was not always solved by a single campaign. In four percent of the projects four different campaigns were required; in ten percent, three campaigns were necessary. As might be expected, those communities eliciting funds through formal appropriations by civil bodies were most successful with one intense period of effort. This effort was, of course, directed to the task of convincing local governing officials that the hospital was a necessary facility for the community. In the event of more than one campaign, the evidence shows that seldom was the same method of fund-raising employed twice in succession. The most usual pattern was that of initiating with a voluntary gift campaign under local leadership, and then, with insufficient contributions on hand, to move to civil bodies for formal appropriations from public revenues.

Community Appeals

IN SOME ways the campaign was only a method of appealing to the community in order to encourage interest, loyalties, and the participation of community people. Appeals included a wide range of slogans that were distributed through various communication media. Two frequently used slogans were: "Health is a community responsibility"; and "Let's make the community a better place to live in." In some areas of the United States appeals and slogans dealt with the well-being of one's person or family, personal prestige in contributing money, and the implication of community disaster if hospital facilities remained absent. Some community campaigns exercised the symbol of over-all community solidarity, i. e., "Everyone else in the community is behind it, so why not you?" Most commonly, the use of slogans attempted to stimulate voluntary giving. The 218 reporting projects stressed apparent dangers in evoking the hysteria of fear as a method of gaining support. They reported greater success with appeals directed to community improvement and responsibility. The more subtle appeals were not used to justify a fund-raising campaign to the community. The "behind-the-scenes" negotiations of leaders in the project evoked this more skillful employment of symbols for persuasion and, not infrequently, coercion.[T-8]

Appeals to the community were disseminated by the usual communication media. Of greatest importance were street corner discussion and persuasion. As found in Figure 3, 80 percent of the 218 projects reported the intensive use of face-to-face contact in promoting the idea of the hospital. No less important was the use of newspaper articles and speeches to organized groups. Some projects developed house bills, posters, and radio programs, and a few employed relevant motion pictures.

In developing the campaign organization, the numbers of participating personnel varied widely. There were three popular patterns: organizations with fewer than ten participating persons, those with 30 to 50 persons, and those with more than 100 participants. The projects electing the bond issue tended to have small numbers of active participants, while the assistance of a professional fund-raiser produced a complex campaign organization staffed by large numbers of personnel. This and later evidence provides the clue that the distinguishing characteristic of a campaign directed by a professional fund-raiser is an extensive mobilization of human resources within an organization functioning as a temporary bureaucracy.

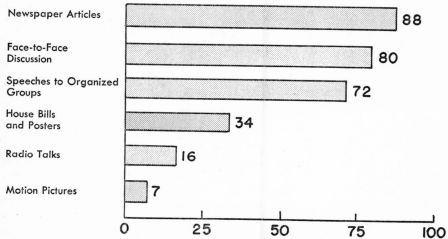

FIGURE 3. Comparative Use by Percent Reporting of Communication Media by 218 Hospital Projects

Use of Consultants

THE 218 projects found it important to glean the experiences of others. In one-third of the projects, community leaders traveled to other communities to learn what had happened in other hospital projects. To supplement Hill-Burton appraisals, one-third of the reporting projects employed a community survey to fix the extent of need for hospital facilities. The majority of the projects asked for and received technical assistance from professional agencies. To a surprising extent, the initiation of this pattern was from within rather than from without the community. Only five percent of the projects reported assistance by college or university specialists. This fact indicates that hospital programs in small communities have not yet seen in the institutions of higher learning a major source of assistance for organizational and educational functions.

Finally, nine out of ten projects recommended the careful use of community surveys and outside consultants as worthy devices. This was most true, as reported, in the detailed planning of the actual construction. All of the projects reported that outside consultants were most greatly utilized after sufficient funds were obtained and the architectural aspects of the project commenced. The evidence suggests that the initiation and organizational features of the hospital quest were conspicuously free of professional assistance from without the community. However, most projects found endless consultation necessary on the details of site selection, blueprint development, the actual construction, and the requirements of hospital ownership and administration.

Not always as simple as it might seem was the usual final step of the promotion campaign. After the busy details of initiation, forming sponsorship, developing campaigns, and raising the hospital building, came the task of settling the ownership of the hospital. The favored types of ownership reported were those of county ownership, non-profit hospital associations, and municipal ownership (42 percent, 40 percent, and 14 percent, respectively). Again, 33 Far West projects were incorporated under respective Hospital Districts.[T-9]

Bonds or Dollars

HILL-BURTON hospital projects in small towns and rural communities may be classified in two groups: those sponsored by already-existing hospital associations or by associations newly formed for the purpose; and those related to the jurisdictional efforts of county and municipal civil governing bodies. Among these, the extent of the connection with local governmental structure appeared to be the greatest determining factor of the style of community acion toward the hospital goal. Forty-six of the 218 reporting projects were sponsored by either a county or a municipal governing body. Sponsorship by some group other than a civil one, largely hospital boards and associations, accounted for 126 projects. The remaining 46 projects failed to report the sponsorship type or reported a type not identifiable in the two present classifications.

A project sponsored by civil government went through legally formalized events. In such projects, members of operating committees were selected in one-half the cases through appointment by local officials. This occurred in only one in five projects sponsored by associations. Almost seven out of ten of the projects electing sponsorship by civil government chose the bond issue to raise money; and but 30 percent of the projects with association sponsorship did so. For the latter projects, the voluntary public subscription was the leading method of raising funds.[T-10]

The final ownership of the hospital grew from the arrangements by which it was achieved. As Table 1 shows, more than eight in ten of the projects sponsored by civil government resulted in county or municipal ownership. Only four in ten of the projects sponsored by associations ended with public ownership. The remainder were operated as non-profit associations.

There were variations in the problems met in the community arena between projects sponsored by civil government and those sponsored by hospital associations and boards. Both types of projects did, however, encounter similar internal disagreements, and the resistance of medical doctors. The civil government projects met with greater difficulty over threatened high taxes than did those projects which, through association sponsorship, selected the voluntary subscription, rather than the bond issue, as a fund-raising device. In

Table 1

Characteristic	Civil Government Projects Percent	Voluntary Association Projects Percent
Members of operating groups appointed by local officials	49	20
Bond issue as fund-raising method	63	30
County or municipal ownership	81	41

addition, the conflict between municipalities within the hospital service area was considerably greater when the hospital project was oriented to the county and under sponsorship of a county governing body. Conversely, those projects sponsored by associations encountered more difficulty in the reported "lack of leadership", and "resistance from people in outlying areas."

The extent to which appeals and communication to the community were employed in the midst of campaigns indicates the scope of the community action plan. Projects sponsored by hospital associations employed a consistently greater use of communication media and appeals than did civil government projects. The use of news articles, personal discussion and persuasion, speeches to organized groups, house bills and posters, and motion pictures—all these were evidently more necessary for the hospital project sponsored by the specialized board or association. In this way, the project with sponsorship by the association or board appeared to be the more busy one. Informing the public was more commonly practiced. Too, appealing to the personal responsibilities of the citizen was more extensive, whereas the civil government project utilized more general appeals with a broad community orientation.

In spite of this, however, the project sponsored by civil government was the more decisive one. Success after one campaign occurred for seven out of ten such projects as compared with five in ten of the others. Almost half of the projects sponsored by hospital associations required as many as four successive campaigns, while those with a direct connection with civil government required more than one campaign in only three of ten projects. An even better clue to the difference which sponsorship makes in the character of community action is that of numbers of actively participating workers in the project. Association sponsored projects surpassed by far those of civil government in the extent of participation by local people. One-third of the projects with association sponsorship reported more than 75 participating personnel. In only one-tenth of the civil government projects did this occur.

In Retrospect

PROGRESS of various communities toward the hospital goal presents readily visible similarities and dissimilarities, as does all local action in comparable communities. Certain minimum essentials characterized the efforts of the 218 reporting projects. In all projects there was the prerequisite of hospital need. Community leaders, with few exceptions, were aware of these needs and employed them widely in early informal negotiations, securing the approval of influential organizations, and bringing about a specified form of sponsoring group. Then, too, no project escaped a minimum set of sequential events. First among them, of course, was the essential of fixing the responsibility for the project, the locus of sponsorship. Next was the choice of method for raising money. In some ways the hospital project, from the vantage point of comparison of community action, was synonymous with the method of collecting funds. Although the methods differed, every project had to scale the obstacle of gaining large sums of money, the amount often seeming to be almost unattainable. In many of the communities of present interest, the hundreds of thousands of dollars necessary for a single institution represented the most foreboding task to which the community had historically been committed. It is not surprising that the translation of the hospital into figures of finance called forth attacks from irate citizens and clubs, with cries that "the hospital is not needed," "let's add to the old one," "why not wait awhile?," "taxes are ruining the community," "the hospital won't pay for itself after we have it," and "why should we pay for the doctors' workshop?".

Numerous discussions with local citizens, encouraged by the research teams, led to the inference that community leaders for the hospital projects frequently were so intent on building the hospital that they overlooked the hospital operations to follow. In many instances, local people had come to believe that the big task was to gain the physical structure of the hospital. The rest would take care of itself. Yet, for every instance of a problem solved, there was a new problem of finance or administration, once the structure was dedicated. The frequent unexpected consequence of what to do with the hospital stems from the preoccupation of raising funds to build it, often to the total exclusion of its future as a newly-won institution of the community.

Every project had its trials in blueprinting the architectural design of the hospital. Committee after committee, meeting after meeting, and revision after revision—these measured the rigor of deciding the number of bassinets, allocations to the operating room, and the width of the halls. More often than not, the planners had to withstand the rebuke of the citizenry that the hospital was too big, too fancy, too much decor, too much expense. Thus it will be, for right or for wrong, that many a community will keep its grudge against the "government architect" who "talked us into more than we needed." Then, too, rising building costs after World War II became an obsession to communities which, with building funds on hand, found them successively inadequate. Indeed, it is not strange that the emotional aftermath and the continuation of anxieties showed on the faces of men and women along Main Street who assumed the burden of organization, of funds, of construction, and of operation. Yet, the final dedication ceremony erased most of the gossip and bickering, and the endless nights of committee sessions, as many reported.

Most striking in the 218 projects was the uniformity of leadership. Throughout the small towns of America, this leadership was provided by the men who manage the stores and shops and banks along Main Street. Although farm people and their organizations were indispensable, the hospital turned out to be the major concern of the businessman. The hospital was dollars and cents, budgets, architects, accounting ledgers, and financial agreements. It was not welfare, nor was it only civic responsibility for the sake of making the community a better place in which to live. It was trips to the state capitol and arguments with the county Board of Supervisors. The hospital was not like the easy agreements of doing good for one's home town. It was "sticking one's neck out." The people who did so were, for the most part, neither farmers, social workers, nor doctors. They were the people who knew about dollars and banks and bookkeeping. They were the people who knew about the wealth of the community and, for the most part, possessed it.

Yet, the differences in community action initiated and multiplied depending on which gate of sponsorship the local task entered. Thus, the basic choice of hospital building was that of casting, or not casting, the process into the sponsorship of civil government. Some did and some did not. For those that did, the work to follow was formally legal, involved less public relations, and reduced the need to appeal to citizen responsibilities—but was more decisive. For those which did not, extensive community arrangements developed, newspaper articles and public meetings increased, other towns became competitive, and chances of having to stop and start all over again increased. Only the future may reveal which gate leads to the clearest expression of satisfactory hospital service, and the extent to which the hospital is supported and nurtured by the public which it serves.

III. PREVENTING AND PAYING

COMMUNITY action for local health departments and cooperative prepayment plans compares with hospital developments in many ways. Yet, at some points, the respective processes vary. The present chapter delineates some important dissimilarities in community quests for health departments and cooperative prepayment plans, not only between them but in contrast to hospital projects. For example, although the major stages of community action are applicable to both health department and prepayment plan developments, the use of certain organizational methods differ. Thus, a definite period for a "campaign," as in hospital projects, does not occur significantly. For the following contrast, the reports of 51 recently-organized local health departments and the evidence from 18 cooperative prepayment plans will be employed.

Early Community Situations

ACTIVE interest in either the health department or the cooperative prepayment plan flows, of course, from situations of community need, actual or believed. The hospital project eventually reached compliance with Hill-Burton provisions. The readiness for community action toward the other two goals was subject to the permissive or restrictive provisions of legislation.[1] Permissible patterns of developing health departments frequently vary from state to state. In addition, the health department is a venture which relates to a prescribed jurisdictional unit, which is in the present study the county. The chartering of rural cooperative organizations to provide medical care is also fraught with frequent restrictive measures. The concentration of cooperative prepayment plans in the Southwest indicates the specific conditions of early community situations.[2]

The delays in initiating action toward the health department and the prepayment plan were as extensive as those for hospitals. Extensive periods of discussion preceded first attempts to organize the community for the respective goals. Prepayment plan organizations apparently required longer periods of preparatory discussion, for the eighteen projects reported not less than three years of time lapse between first interest and initial action. Half of the plans delayed initiation for more than nine years after the beginning of interest and community discussion. The causes of delay for the prepayment plan projects were similar to those for hospital projects—inadequate funds, a lack of community interest, and the advent of World War II. Most delays in initiating health department services appeared to be caused indirectly by reported inadequate funds. The lack of support by county governing bodies and the lack of interest in preventive health measures by local citizens were reported by two-thirds of the 51 health department projects.[T-11]

Although no case studies were made of health department and prepayment plan projects, the reported comments do suggest certain inferences. Early delays in initiating a local health department were related to insufficient health education, especially dealing with the purposes, possibilities, and costs of preventive health measures. Frequently coupled to this lack of knowledge and enthusiasm was a core of resistance centered actively in the county governing body, and passively in certain city-centered associations. In other instances, even the presence of widespread interest and a receptive governing body was thwarted by a lack of willing county-wide leadership in position to assume the responsibilities of sponsorship. Particularly in the experience of the 51 health department organizations does an old difficulty in community organization apply: that one explanation for initiatory faltering in community achievement may be found in the extent of meaningful mass education just prior to the formal initiation of community activity.

Initiation of Action

HOSPITALS, local health departments, and cooperative prepayment plans do not result until the ideas are translated into community tasks. To move from an idea to a task requires initiators. Someone or some group must channel community readiness into purposeful action. As did the hospital projects, the 18 reporting prepayment plans revealed that initiation could be credited to individual persons acting without direct reference to formal organizations. Initiation by an organized community or county group was not reported. However, the initiators for health department projects were, for 20 of the 51 cases, organized groups. The evidence suggests that an explanation for this occurrence may be that the principal target of health department organizations is the appropriate county governing body. The initial approach, as found by the 51 cases, was best made by an organized group with county-wide prestige.[T-12]

A continuing analysis of the initiation process reveals the most startling difference in community action toward the three goals. As previously described, the occupational affiliation of initiators and active participants for hospital projects was primarily that of business, i. e., self-employed businessmen, employed executives, and professionals, including physicians. The 18 prepayment plans reported a similar occurrence, but with a lower incidence of self-employed businessmen and a higher incidence of professionals. The participation of physicians was reported only to a negligible extent.

The health department projects differed significantly. First of all, while hospitals and prepayment plans were guided almost entirely by men, health department ventures found women taking roles of active participation. Seventeen percent of 175 participants ranked "most active" in the 51 health department organizations were housewives. Only one in ten of the 175 participants were self-employed businessmen. Forty-five percent were professionals and ten percent were physicians. As compared with hospital projects, all other occupational classifications were low.

Among the professional workers actively involved in the health department projects, school teachers and administrators, nurses, and local agricultural officials were most frequently cited. Finally, a comment is required about the incidence of farm owners and operators. Health department organizations were relatively low in number of farmers as "most active" participants, with six percent of the 175 persons so ranked. Farmers were "most active" in the prepayment plan projects, however, to the extent of 20 percent. In the latter instance the experience of farm people with rural cooperatives undoubtedly is a contributing explanation.

Sponsorship

HOSPITAL projects were primarily sponsored by hospital associations and local county or municipal governing bodies. The cooperative prepayment plans, usually adjuncts of cooperative hospitals, followed this pattern. Seven of the 18 reporting plans were sponsored by a hospital association or board. Not a single prepayment plan listed civil government as the centrally important locus of sponsorship. Conversely, health department organizations cited civil governing groups as sponsors to the extent of 45 percent. In both health department and prepayment plan organizations, sponsoring groups were more often community or county councils, including health councils, than in the case of hospitals. Fourteen percent of the health departments were sponsored by a local health council.[3] Six of the 18 prepayment plan cases were sponsored by county-wide farm organizations—a contrast to the experience with hospitals (three percent) and local health departments (six percent).

The development of health departments frequently has civil governing

Table 2

OCCUPATIONAL POSITION OF PERSONS NAMED "MOST ACTIVE"
IN MAJOR HEALTH FACILITIES PROJECTS

Occupation	Hospital	Health Departments	Prepayment Plans
	Percent	Percent	Percent
Self-employed businessman	34	9	18
Professional	18	46	28
Medical doctor	10	10	3
Employed manager	16	4	17
Farm owner or operator	10	6	20
Civil official	8	6	3
Non-supervisory employee	4	2	5
Housewife	–	17	6
Total Percent	100	100	100
Total Number	670	175	56

groups and health councils as centrally important sponsoring agents. Co-operative prepayment plans favor related hospital associations and farm organizations. The importance of the health council to health department development provides an inference that citizens' groups devoted specifically to health affairs are more likely to assume tasks of preventive health than the major physical facility of the hospital. One might expect a specialized sponsoring arrangement because the health department is legally instituted within formal jurisdictional units.

The Problems of Sponsorship

DISAGREEMENTS between members of the sponsoring groups for health department and prepayment plan projects were similar to those for hospital developments. Seventeen percent of the health departments and prepayment plans reported professional and lay disagreements within the sponsoring group. In several cases, an inability to ascertain the attitude of the local medical society was a factor in resulting differences of opinion.

In order to explore the problems of health department development, 318 health officers in the United States responded to a supplementary poll. One in five of the reporting health officers believed that "conflicts with the organized medical profession" constitute an opportunity for disagreement. Added comments provided the inference that the medical profession would support the local health department plan if other major goals were not simultaneously pursued. One case provided a rather commonly-found statement, "Doctors were first in favor of a county hospital rather than a health unit, but agreed to support a health unit after the county commission turned down the proposal for a hospital."

Community and county problems for hospital projects were largely those of conflict between neighboring towns or counties. Although the prepayment plans reported similar instances, health department organizations did not experience inter-municipal conflict. Instead, half of the 51 reporting health departments listed their major community or county problem as the beliefs that the project was unnecessary. In 14 percent of the 51 cases, the problem of conflicts between town and country was reported. Both health department and prepayment plan organizations experienced more commonly than hospital projects a "lack of skilled persons and not enough good leadership" (45 percent and 67 percent, respectively).

Sixteen percent of the 318 reporting health officers believed that a common problem of developing a health department is the public judgment that the project is "political." By this they meant that influential persons and organizations frequently concluded that the effort toward a health department was the special interest of another. Hence, disagreement and divisiveness would occur.

Hospital projects, as previously reported, encountered some difficulty with influential persons and community organizations. Both health departments and prepayment plans reported fewer problems with individuals, but ran into the opposition of organized groups. This finding relates, of course, to the reported form of initiation for both health departments and prepayment plans as organized groups within the community.

The following quotations may provide an indication of the problems met with persons and groups within the community for health department projects: "One leader of a political party felt it was leading to socialized medicine" . . . . "Some said that the lack of public health personnel made it unnecessary to organize the health department" . . . . "Many believed that it was getting to the place where there would be insufficient funds to carry on all phases of county government" . . . . "For us, opposition equalled misunderstanding on the part of the medical profession and fears over money on the part of our Board of Supervisors" . . . . "We had, at first, an almost total lack of understanding as to public health needs and the benefits to be derived from a health department" . . . . "A former nurse built up opposition through influential friends" . . . . "Too many of our organizations wanted to get their finger in the pie."

The reporting health officers also provided a variety of statements which not only serve as reminders, but as cautions, to the sponsoring group initiating a local health department: "Make certain every organization is represented in the early planning" . . . . "Don't overlook the idea that public health is designed only for the care of charity patients" . . . . "The enthusiastic leader for the public health department may unwittingly criticise the medical profession. This can lead to real trouble" . . . . "Watch out for the individually

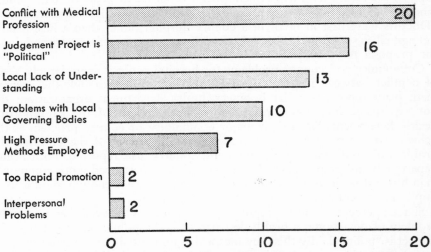

FIGURE 4. Percentage Incidence of Health Officer Recommendations of Problems To Be Avoided in Organizing Health Departments

employed nurses of voluntary health associations" . . . . "Public health has to be sold to the community by good education rather than forcing it through with a small group of community zealots" . . . . "A lot of organizations don't settle the rumors that the health department is 'something for free' " . . . .

38

"Somehow the public health idea falls into the trap of opposing political factions in city and county government. This has to be overcome by a wise beginning" . . . . "A common problem is rushing toward official action before there is adequate community understanding" . . . . "Public health developments often have too many commanders and too few leaders" . . . . "An early fault is sometimes building the health unit around one person or group" . . . . "A real trouble is often brewed by professional public health personnel working directly for units rather than intelligent lay organizations and individuals" . . . . "All is lost if existing health and medical services in the community are undersold by the leaders in the organization of a local health unit."

Resistance, if not direct opposition, by organized groups to health department projects came most often from the appropriate county governing body. The usual explanation is that county finances could not adequately support the kind of public health services deemed necessary by the initiating groups or persons. The prepayment plan found difficulty in the failure of other organizations within nearby communities to support the prepayment plan through promised memberships. Seven of the reporting 18 prepayment plan projects experienced a lack of support by organized groups in nearby communities. One writer has suggested that a wise procedure is not to name the prepayment plan project in specific terms of any one community. To do so may retard the cooperation of adjoining communities that fall within the service area for which the plan is intended.

Organizational Methods

THE method-evoking question for hospital, public health department, and prepayment plan projects to decide was that of present or potential financial investment. Health department developments had to persuade local governing bodies that public health services were important enough for the appropriation of funds. Cooperative prepayment plan projects were consistently confronted with some reactions from lay and professional people that the plan might not adequately and soundly provide for the costs for medical and health care. The major similarity in achieving the three major health facilities was the attention required by community organizational plans to countering the arguments of community residents that the project was a present or potential financial risk. For the most part, therefore, the organizational methods employed in the respective projects were geared to solving resistances which had developed around the theme of financial risk. Attention to Figure 5 will provide the contrast found in the experiences of achieving the three types of major health facilities.

An over-view of the organizational methods employed by health department and prepayment projects indicates that, as in the hospital projects, the general procedure was directed both toward individuals and organizations within the community. Seldom were promotional campaigns oriented only to influential persons. No more frequent was an organizational plan dependent only on groups with prestige in the community or county. Based on the testimony of project reports, the recommendation was made repeatedly that

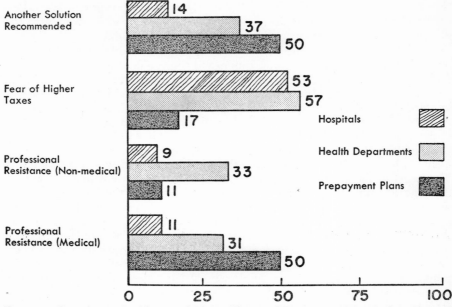

FIGURE 5. Percentage Incidence of Major Types of Resistance Stimulating Organizational Plans

achieving a hospital, health department, or prepayment plan depended greatly on establishing long-range and short-range objectives. These could be pursued methodically. The testimonials infer that local people soon found that success depended on a re-definition of the particular health facility aim into such specific goals as raising money, carrying on an educational program, negotiating with governing officials, visiting other communities for consultation, and assigning specific jobs to particular groups and individuals.

Regardless of the type of health facility taken as the goal, some stage of the project was an intense effort commonly called a campaign. For the hospital projects the campaign was actually a plan to raise sufficient funds in a brief period of time. As the reports from the health department projects indicated, the campaign marked the climax of the community proceedings, frequently in the form of negotiations with respective county governing bodies to obtain an adequate appropriation for health services. The campaign for the health departments was actually one of promotion. The reporting projects differ, however, in their definitions of the intense period of effort or campaign. Some campaigns aimed to persuade the appropriate governing body that sufficient funds should be forthcoming to subsidize recommended health services. Other projects spent their intense period of effort on a program of education throughout the community in order to establish a greater awareness of public health services. One-third of the reporting health department projects were unable to explain the objectives of the campaign period. Of those reporting on this question, however, five in ten listed the "persuasion of the local governing body" as the objective; and four in ten cited the "educational efforts to create understanding of public health services."

The reports of health department projects indicated that a sustained period of interest is necessary for successfully organizing a local health department. Although the period of intense activity for such organizations was more extensive than that for hospital projects, four out of ten health department cases believed that the important factor in their success was a single intense effort. Five out of ten of the health department cases also believed that securing a health department should be the only major community or county task during the period of sustained interest. Earlier references to problems met by health department developments indicate that the task of gaining a local health department cannot commonly confront the divided loyalties which occur when another major facility such as a hospital is also under consideration.

The three types of major community health projects employed a wide range of slogans and appeals in the community organization scheme. Hospital projects utilized slogans which implied "community responsibility" and "making the community a better place in which to live." Health department campaigns employed more specific slogans and appeals, usually a rephrasing of the potential contributions of the local health department. Hence, "better sanitation" and "better prevention of sickness" were widely used slogans and appeals. The cooperative prepayment plan projects correspond closely with hospital projects in the use of specific slogans and appeals. Two-thirds of the reporting plans used the additional argument that "a successful prepayment plan will attract medical personnel to the community." Seventeen of the 18 reporting prepayment plans also emphasized that considerable stress was placed on community or local responsibility. Hence, a major slogan employed was: "Health improvement is a county or community responsibility."

The use of the usual media for communicating to the community was similar, for health departments and prepayment plans, to the hospital developments. Sponsoring groups for the three types of facilities preferred to employ a wide variety of media rather than limit the local organizational schemes to one. As was the case for hospital projects, health department and prepayment plan organizations accented face-to-face discussion and persuasion. Where 80 percent of the hospital projects employed face-to-face discussion, health department organizations reported this use to the extent of 68 percent, and 77 percent of the prepayment plans so reported.

Public Relations Techniques

NEWSPAPER articles were also fully employed. The hospital projects depended on newspaper publicity most commonly, the prepayment plans were intermediate in its usage, and the least usage, reported by 59 percent of the cases, was by the health department projects. All three types of projects made considerable use of speeches to organized groups and, to a lesser extent, of radio presentations. County-wide mass meetings were employed in the health department organizations, but were not reported by either hospital or prepayment plan projects. The prepayment plan projects also utilized a device which was not often reported by either the hospital or health department projects. Eleven of the 18 reporting prepayment plan projects developed an illustrated brochure. This device summarized the purposes of the prepayment plan and was frequently distributed throughout the community for discussion. The use of previously printed materials for publicity was not commonly reported by either hospital or health department projects. An exception is found in those hospital projects which employed a professional fund-raiser. In these instances, the fund-raising campaign employed a greater number of printed pamphlets, letters, reporting forms, and enclosures.

Health department projects employed consistently less use of the various communication media, with the exception of considerable attention given to county-wide mass meetings. The size of the jurisdictional unit for health departments and the relatively larger number of members in the sponsoring group were given as reasons why this occurred. Either wide appeal was considered unnecessary or it was rendered difficult.

Persuading Key People

THE reporting health department projects showed that a necessary aid to successful achievement is an active and helpful state health department. Eliciting the cooperation of "exceptional" persons in the community was deemed essential, as well as gaining the approval of "strong" and "high prestige" organizations. City-centered associations of civic and service functions were believed most essential for gaining approval.

The cooperative prepayment plan communities, while following the experiences of the 218 reporting Hill-Burton hospital projects, reported a higher incidence of the use of college specialists. One-fourth of the 18 plans stated that assistance had been rendered by college workers. The extreme rurality of the prepayment plan communities undoubtedly had brought them into close contact with local representatives of state colleges. More than half of the prepayment plan projects utilized a community survey. The purpose was to learn about local health needs and determine the extent of local interest in the cooperative prepayment plan as a device for solving the costs of health care.

Eight in ten of the 18 reporting prepayment plan projects had reviewed the experiences of other communities. Several of the plans referred to the influence and assistance of an original development at Elk City, Oklahoma.[5] Initiatory phases of the plans were frequently assisted by representatives from the Oklahoma organization and from the Cooperative Health Federation of America.

The number of persons participating in the active phases of the projects varied. For the most part, actively participating persons in the hospital projects were few in number. An exception occurs in those instances of the employment of a professional fund-raiser. Prepayment plan projects were similar to hospitals. However, the number of participating persons for health department developments was relatively larger. In two out of ten reporting projects, the number of active participants was given as more than 125 persons.

As reported earlier, the hospital projects selected members of sponsoring groups largely through appointments by local officials and community elections. Only 18 percent of the hospital projects reported that local community organizations had been requested to appoint a member to serve on the sponsoring body. However, health department projects did make this request. Three in ten of the projects had gained their sponsoring group members by appointments from community organizations. One-third of the health departments also reported that membership on the sponsoring group was entirely voluntary.

Prepayment plan projects employed two predominant methods of selecting members for sponsoring groups. One-half of the plans utilized appointments from community organizations. The other half used, for the most part, the method of community elections. Eight of the reporting plans included medical doctors as members of sponsoring groups. Ten prepayment plans did not.

The majority of the hospital projects and prepayment plans reported that the sponsoring body was organized to work for the particular project. The groups, therefore, had no history of previous sponsorship of other community projects. However, the health department projects reported in two-thirds of the cases that the sponsoring group had been active in previous community activities. As shown by other evidence, the hospitals and prepayment plans apparently require specific forms and patterns of organization. The health department produces a sponsoring arrangement that tends to be more diverse. A greater variety of local organizations become concerned, and there are a multiplicity of administrative units to be reckoned with. Thus, a continuing body in the community, such as the health council, may appear more appropriate in initiating and completing the successful organization of the health department.[4]

Contrasts Among Projects

HOSPITALS, local health departments, and cooperative prepayment plans are all major health facilities. Yet, the ways in which small communities acquire each facility are different. Even with the same class of community problems, the methods employed to mobilize local resources may need to differ. The health department developments commonly vary the most.

Certain elements of community action were present in all three types of projects. Each associated community began action with some appreciation of need, brought about by crisis, education, and persuasion. Once community action was initiated, local government was a potential aid to hospital and health department projects, but not for prepayment plans. All of the projects organized community action through voluntary assistance rather than paid help. Most of the reports considered that this was as it should be. The most general problem met by the three types of projects was a lack of leadership and experienced persons. The type of project did not greatly affect the incidence of problems dealing with resistances by portions of the concerned community. Putting into operation a new hospital, a health department, or a prepayment plan made necessary the use of technical and other aids within and without the community.

The differences in the community action schemes were few in number, but some are important to recall. Individuals and informal groups of individuals received credit for initiating hospitals and prepayment plans. Organized groups were credited with successfully initiating local efforts toward the health department. Especially in the initiatory phases, the development of hospitals was an activity centered in the towns, with men as leaders. Health department and prepayment plan developments moved more to the rural areas for early initiation, and women enjoyed more active participation.

The salient difference in the three projects was found in the occupational positions of the leaders. Two-thirds of the most active leaders for hospital projects were self-employed businessmen, professionals, or employed executives. Professional persons and housewives were credited with performing the task of acquiring a local health department. Farmers enjoyed relatively greater participation in the prepayment plan projects. Likewise, farm organizations came into sponsorship with the prepayment plans.

The sponsoring group for the hospital or prepayment plan was commonly small, and formed specifically for the project. The sponsoring group for the health department project was larger, and less specifically but more informally organized for the duties of the project. Becoming a member of the sponsoring group for hospitals and prepayment plans depended largely on official appointment by local governing bodies, or by election at community meetings. Becoming a member of the sponsoring group for the health departments depended on appointment to represent community organizations. Such representation on the sponsoring body for the health departments was therefore frequently gained by voluntary participation.

Hospital and prepayment plan projects utilized short and intensive campaign periods. Health department projects reported promotional campaigns that were longer in duration and less intense. In addition, the health department developments did not emphasize the use of communication media as did the other two types. Getting a health department did, however, make necessary the programming of county-wide mass meetings, a procedure less used by the other two developments.

Working toward a hospital, as differentiated from providing organized public health services for the community or county is, the evidence suggests, interpreted differently by the community-at-large. The hospital, to many local people across the country, is construed as falling within the "institution" of business. The health department is construed as falling within the "institution" of welfare. Hence, the original impetus toward either calls forth from the community differing kinds of leaders, varying forms of sponsorship, and dissimilar types of methods. The hospital finds ready acceptance along Main Street. The hospital stimulates the men who know about construction, money, bookkeeping, and law. The health department stimulates the men and women who want to prevent sickness, and who worry about children, cleanliness, physical examinations, and teeth. The hospital idea is carried by the man who leaves his desk at the bank or the business house and goes to see an official of the hospital building program. The health department idea is carried, more often, by the housewife who removes her apron and goes to a county meeting.

iv. REGION AND PROCESS

THE CONSIDERED evaluation that ". . . . the plantation system for generations has permitted only a relatively few to initiate action, to make decisions, or to engage in concerted community action" comes from the distinguished work of two rural sociologists, Charles P. Loomis and J. Allan Beegle. It is one of many observations which set the South apart as exhibiting its own style of solving community problems.[1] A major proposal of the present study was to identify the styles of community attack in various parts of the United States toward the same goal. The goal was that of the hospital.

The essentials for a new hospital did not vary widely. Wherever the hospitals came into being, they were preceded by concern with dollars, bonds, sites, bricks, federal assistance, architects, and local government. The physical and economic ingredients of the hospital were much the same in the deep South, along the mountain areas of the West, amidst the prairies of the Great Plains, in the densely populated areas of the Middle West, and throughout the urbanized Northeast. The important question concerned the social ingredients. Given the same goal, the hospital, to what extent did small American communities approach the task in the same way? Even more important were the differences in approach.

This chapter follows the hospital-getting process across the country. Again it is a story of contrasts. The contrasts are between six regional groupings of hospital projects, those in the Southeast, the Southwest, the Middle States, the Far West, the Northwest, and the Northeast. Fifty-two projects reported from the Southeast; 25 from the Southwest; 58 from the Middle States; 19 from the Far West; 40 from the Northwest; and 24 from the Northeast.

Civil and Voluntary Sponsorship

ACQUIRING a hospital required varying styles of community action in these six regions of the United States. Variations occurred step by step, method by method, and problem by problem. Yet, the greatest variations occurred between the extreme of predominance of civil government and the other events linked with it; and the heavy incidence of voluntary sponsorship and support with related events. The gate of sponsorship through which the hospital project entered made a difference. This difference carried over into recognizable styles of community action, exhibited by the regional groupings of projects.

Five characteristics of the community action scheme for hospital projects, with specific attention to the decision-making process, were assumed to be not only important guideposts for action, but to be interrelated so as to con-

45

stitute an over-all style of attack. These were the nature of the sponsoring group, the manner in which members were named to the sponsoring and operating bodies for the hospital, the extent to which civil officials were active in the project, the type of fund-raising method employed, the number of participants actively associated with the project, and, finally, the type of ownership eventually elected for the hospital.

Table 3

COMPARISON OF THE INCIDENCE OF CIVIL GOVERNMENT
CHARACTERISTICS IN REGIONAL GROUPINGS OF HOSPITAL PROJECTS

Civil Government Characteristic	Region					
	South-east	South-west	Far West	Middle States	North-west	North-east
	Percent					
Civil government as sponsoring agent	38	36	11	19	10	0
Members of sponsoring and/or operating groups appointed by civil government	36	36	33	20	12	8
Civil officials as active persons	10	8	6	10	9	3
Bond issue as the fund-raising method	60	68	61	67	53	13
County or municipal ownership	61	76	50	67	52	12
Personnel in the project (10 or less reported)	17	24	11	12	13	4

The Southeast and the Southwest regions favored civil governing bodies as sponsoring groups. Almost four in ten of the 77 projects in the two regions were sponsored by official civil government, largely by the county governing bodies. Conversely, not a single reporting project from the Northeast was sponsored by a civil governing body. Both the Far West and the Northwest projects were relatively less often sponsored by civil government (11 and 10 percent, respectively). Attention to Table 3 will reveal that the Southeast and the Northeast projects differ most widely in the use of civil government as centrally important sponsors. Similar to the Southeast projects are those of the Southwest. The projects of the Middle States correspond more closely with the two southern regions than do those of the Far West and the Northwest.

The methods of naming members to sponsoring or operating groups varied in much the same way as did the type of centrally important sponsoring group. Although variation occurred between the five regional grouping of projects, it was the Southeast and the Southwest that more commonly secured members for sponsoring and operating groups through official appointment. Only three percent of the Northeast projects utilized official appointments to obtain participants.

Attention to Table 3 indicates that the five regional groupings of projects compare closely in the degree of incidence of civil officials as active participants, employing the bond issue as the fund-raising method, and county or municipal ownership. The consistent exception is the Northeast. An assumption was made that a constellation of characteristics dealing with civil government, or at least with certain offices of immediate importance, would be found where there were relatively few participants. Thus, it is not surprising that projects with a high incidence of such characteristics reported more commonly a low number of active participants in the hospital-getting task.

However, 126 of the reporting 218 projects elected some other form of sponsorship than civil government. The predominant type was the hospital association and board. Certain characteristics were again related to this voluntary style of community action, specifically the decision-making process. Although hospital associations or boards were popular sponsoring agents, their greatest incidence was in the Northeast. The voluntary selection of members to sponsoring and operating groups, through appointment at community meetings, occurred more commonly in the Northeast and the Northwest, and least commonly in the Far West and the Southeast.

Attention to Table 4 reveals similar relationships between the five regional groupings of projects. The Northeast hospital projects exhibited a greater incidence of voluntary characteristics than did the other regional groupings, especially in contrast with the two southern regions. It followed on this that the incidence of specific sponsoring groups, formed to sponsor only the hospital, was greater in the Northeast. Self-employed businessmen were actively involved among the high-ranked participants in each of the six regions, but their greatest incidence was in the Northeast, and their lowest incidence in the Southeast. The ownership of the hospital found non-profit associations high (88 percent) in the Northeast, and low in the Fast West, Southwest, and Middle States (17 percent, 24 percent, and 33 percent, respectively). Finally, in half of the Northeast projects, a relatively greater number of participants took part in the project. The Far West exhibited somewhat less high numbers of participants. This was undoubtedly due to the legal instrumentality of the hospital district which was liberally employed in that region.

Hence, each of the two constellations of characteristics, one dealing with civil government, the other with voluntary associations, is actually the reciprocal of the other. In both instances, as Tables 3 and 4 provide, the practices in the southern regions consistently deviate from those of the Northeast. The remaining three regions—the Middle States, the Far West, and the Northwest—fluctuate more widely in regard to these characteristics. However, the Northwest projects tend to correspond somewhat with those of the Northeast.

Table 4

Voluntary Characteristic	Region					
	South-east	South-west	Far West	Middle States	North-west	North-east
	Percent Reporting					
Hospital association or board as sponsoring agent	54	64	39	65	51	83
Members to sponsoring and/or operating groups appointed at community meetings	11	20	6	26	40	33
Organizationally specific sponsoring groups	62	60	61	69	60	88
Self-employed businessmen and employed managers as active participants	45	52	46	46	56	62
Non-profit association ownership	39	24	17	33	48	88
Personnel in the project (76 or more reported)	23	16	5	38	27	50

Problems

THE incidence of various problems met by the regional groupings of projects was generally similar. A few exceptions occurred. The Far West encountered relatively more resistance from professional persons and from influential persons. The incidence of opposition over threat of high taxes also was felt more commonly in the Far West. The Middle States, Southeast, and Southwest followed closely in the incidence of this problem. Conversely, the Northeast projects reported difficulty with opposition over threatened high taxes in only 21 percent of the cases. The Northeast projects, however, experienced difficulty more commonly with two other problems. The first dealt with resistance from outlying areas of the hospital service community. The second problem, also encountered to a considerable degree by other regions, was that of an "insufficient feeling of need" in the respective community.

The use of legal instrumentalities to achieve the hospital was followed by resistance from municipalities within the respective county, as well as by active opposition over threatened high taxes. The voluntary hospital project, employing the municipality and its surrounding trade area as the appropriate unit, encountered more frequently the problems of outlying area resistance, and an insufficient feeling of need. The former were encountered by projects in the two southern regions and in the Far West. The latter were characteristic of the projects in the Northwest and the Northeast.

Table 5

Community Action Problem	Region					
	South-east	South-west	Far West	Middle States	North-west	North-east
	Percent					
Interpersonal problems within sponsoring body	35	40	39	20	40	32
Problems with professionals	4	12	28	7	13	4
Problems with medical doctors	17	12	0	7	13	17
Problems with influentials	44	56	77	29	63	49
Organized groups	11	8	17	12	23	21
High taxes	54	60	72	64	42	21
Disagreement on major policies	4	8	6	2	5	4
Outlying area resistance	14	24	28	29	45	54
Insufficient feeling of need	50	44	55	46	45	54
Intermunicipal conflict	35	28	56	35	65	17
Lack of leadership	31	32	61	27	40	33

Media and appeals

IRRESPECTIVE of the type of hospital project or the type of community action problem encountered, one aid was effective communication to the community-or county-at-large. Gaining the consensus necessary for a successful bond issue or adequate voluntary contributions depended, in part, on developing the hospital idea in many channels of communication as stimuli for discussion. One measure of the interest in widespread communication was provided by the reported use of communication media and appeals to the community.

The use of communication media was more extensive in the Northeast and Northwest projects, and less extensive, as measured by the incidence in reports, in the Southeast and Southwest regions. For instance, 75 percent of the Southeast projects employed news articles about the hospital. Ninety-two percent of the Northeast projects and 95 percent of the Northwest projects so reported. Even greater difference occurred in the use of personal contact and persuasion. Sixty-three percent of the Southeast projects employed personal contact, but 96 percent of the Northeast projects used this device for improving communication. Housebills and posters were not, for the most part, devices of importance, except for some employment in projects in the Northwest and the Middle States. There was only slight use made of motion pictures generally but the Northeast projects reported the most extensive use.

Table 6

Media and Appeals	Region					
	South-east	South-west	Far West	Middle States	North-west	North-east
	Percent					
Media						
News articles	75	84	89	95	95	92
Personal contact	63	84	78	81	93	96
Speeches to organized groups	52	52	99	78	68	92
Housebills and posters	21	0	39	46	53	29
Radio talks	21	24	16	14	5	25
Motion pictures	6	0	6	12	2	13
Appeals						
Community oriented	152*	148	155	147	152	150
Personal oriented	69	84	62	100	108	171

* Represents total accumulated percentages

There was no hospital project which did not employ slogans or other appeals. Table 6, in addition to giving a summary of the communication media employed, indicates the incidence of appeals in the six regions. The total accumulated percentage of projects employing various appeals serves as a crude measure. First of all, community-oriented appeals were used uniformly by the six regional groupings of projects. Such slogans as "Let's make the community a better place to live in" were important to about the same degree in hospital projects in various parts of the United States.

The use of personal-oriented appeals to the community, however, varied in the six regions. Such slogans as "Others are behind the hospital, why not you?" were more commonly employed in the Northwest and the Northeast regions. The Far West, Southeast and Southwest were less likely to employ personal-oriented appeals.

As earlier cited, each hospital project was characterized by at least one intense period of effort, that of the campaign. Since the 218 projects of concern in the present study were all successful efforts, the number of required campaigns serves as one measure of difficulty. About half of the 218 projects obtained sufficient funds after one campaign. However, 24 percent required two campaigns and ten percent required three.

Using the number of campaigns as an indication of difficulty, certain differences occurred between the regional groupings of projects. It was the Northwest grouping of projects which tended to employ more than one campaign to obtain the necessary funds for construction. The Northeast region exhibited projects which also followed with this characteristic pattern. The Southwest, Southeast, and Far West appeared most decisive, perhaps the consequence of legally-constituted instrumentalities to achieve the hospital. The more voluntary hospital projects characteristic of the Northwest and Northeast regions were apparently forced more often to stop and start over again. Thus, they tended to be less decisive.

Table 7

NUMBER OF CAMPAIGNS EMPLOYED IN REGIONAL
GROUPINGS OF HOSPITAL PROJECTS

Number of Campaigns	Region						Total
	South-east	South-west	Far West	Middle States	North-west	North-east	
	Percent						
One	60	72	78	55	35	50	56
Two	19	16	11	26	30	38	24
Three	4	4	6	9	22	12	10
Four or more	2	0	0	5	13	0	4
No reply	15	8	5	5	0	0	6
Total percent	100	100	100	100	100	100	100
Total number	52	25	19	58	40	24	218

In order to summarize the relationship between the foregoing characteristics of regional groupings of hospital projects, attention should be directed to Table 8. For each of the major types of characteristics—civil government characteristics, voluntary characteristics, problems encountered, media and appeals, and number of campaigns—the percentage incidence of each characteristic in regional groupings was placed in rank order. Table 8 summarizes the mean rank of each regional grouping in regard to a major characteristic. For operational purposes the two highest rankings are termed "high"; the middle two rankings are termed "moderate"; and the two lowest rankings are termed "low." Each regional category is listed in order of the mean rank of the five major characteristics.

The hospital projects in the Southwest exhibited the greatest association with civil government, encountered moderate problems in community action, exercised relatively low communication to the community, but met with relatively high success after but one campaign.

The hospital projects in the Northeast contrast sharply with such a profile. The Northeast projects were lowest in association with civil goverment, but highest in voluntary components, encountered moderate problems, exercised the highest degree of communication and appeal to the community, but met with low success in completing the project after one campaign.

The Northwest projects were similar to those of the Northeast. Lowest in association with civil government, they are high in the incidence of voluntary characteristics, high in communicating and appealing to the community. They had the least success with one campaign.

Table 8

SUMMARY OF REGIONAL HOSPITAL PROJECT RANKINGS

Composite Characteristic	Ranking					
	High		Moderate		Low	
Civil government characteristics	Southwest 2.00	Southeast 2.33	Middle States 2.83	Far West 3.50	Northwest 4.33	Northeast 6.00
Voluntary characteristics	Northeast 1.16	Northwest 3.00	Middle States 3.00	Southeast 4.16	Southwest 4.33	Far West 5.33
Problems encountered	Far West 2.27	Northwest 2.54	Northeast 3.73	Southwest 3.73	Southeast 4.28	Middle States 4.54
Use of media and appeals	Northeast 2.00	Northwest 3.00	Middle States 3.37	Far West 3.50	Southwest 4.50	Southeast 4.63
Success after one campaign	Far West 1.00	Southwest 2.00	Southeast 3.00	Middle States 4.00	Northeast 5.00	Northwest 6.00

Note: Each figure is the mean rank of the sum of the ranks of percentage-incidence of respective characteristics in regional groupings of projects.

The hospital projects of the Middle States are moderate in degree of association with civil government, moderate in voluntary characteristics, low on problems encountered, and moderate in the extent of communication and appeal. They had moderate success after but one campaign.

The Far West projects were moderate in association with civil government, lowest in the incidence of voluntary characteristics, highest on problems encountered, moderate in the use of communication and appeal to the community, but had the greatest success after but one campaign.

From this, certain summary conclusions may be derived. The first is that the Northeast and the Northwest hospital projects were generally similar in community organizational settings for the decision-making process. Second, the Southwest and Southeast hospital projects were generally similar in the same respect. The third conclusion is that the projects in the Middle States and Far West regions fluctuated relatively more than the other regions in their community organizational settings and hence were less standardized. The fourth conclusion is that the Middle States hospital projects tended in the same direction as the Northeast and Northwest groupings, while the Far West projects tended in the direction of the Southeast and Southwest projects.

There is a final question of decisiveness in projects related in varying degress to civil government. The present information indicates that as the association with civil government increases, the problems of community organization diminish, the use of communication media and appeals decreases, but there occurs a greater chance for assured success after one campaign. Thus, those hospital projects associated with local civil government tended to be more decisive.

The Southeast and the Northeast

THE foregoing section compared the differences between regional groupings of hospital projects, with particular attention to the association of projects with civil government and to certain voluntary characteristics. Another question of importance must be raised. This question deals with the differences, relating to a comparison of the civil government and voluntary functions, which may occur *within* a particular regional grouping of projects. The assumption is merely that if the civil government and voluntary comparisons are not consistent within a given regional grouping of projects, then other factors must account for the variations treated earlier.

Certain selected characteristics will be employed to indicate the variations within a given regional grouping of projects on the civil government and voluntary comparisons. The Southeast regional grouping of 52 projects will be utilized. At each point they will be contrasted with the 24 projects of the Northeast—already summarized as being largely voluntary in nature.

Table 9 provides a comparison of two civil government components of the civil government projects and the voluntary projects in the Southeast, with all of the projects in the Northeast. The selection of members of operating and sponsoring groups was performed in the civil government projects of the Southeast by local civil officials to the extent of 56 percent of the cases.

Only 23 percent of the Southeast voluntary projects employed this method. For the Northeast, only a small number (eight percent) employed this method of selection.

Seventy-eight percent of the civil government projects in the Southeast reported hospital ownership by either county or municipality. Thirty-five percent of the voluntary projects in the Southeast were so owned. Only 12 percent of the Northeast projects resulted in county or municipal ownership.

Table 9

CIVIL GOVERNMENT AND VOLUNTARY PROJECTS IN THE
SOUTHEAST COMPARED WITH THE PROJECTS OF THE NORTHEAST

Characteristic	Southeast		Northeast
	Civil Government	Voluntary	All Projects
		Percent	
Members of sponsoring or operating body appointed by local civil officials	56	23	8
Ownership by county or municipality	78	35	12
Members of sponsoring or operating body appointed at community meetings	6	15	33
Ownership by non-profit association	11	50	88

In conclusion, the voluntary group of hospital projects in the Southeast was intermediate in procedures to the others of the Southeast and those of the Northeast. This intermediacy was true both of the method of member selection and of final ownership of the hospital.

Continued reference to Table 9 indicates that the same comparison of voluntary characteristics actually constitutes a reciprocal relationship. Hence, the voluntary projects of the Southeast approach the Northeast projects in the use of community meetings in selecting members. Conversely, the civil government projects at the Southeast used but slightly the selection method of appointments at community meetings. However, one-third of the Northeast projects employed this method of member selection. Again, the voluntary projects of the Southeast were intermediate to the other two groupings.

Problems: Consistent variation between regional groupings of hospital projects was not present as to problems encountered. However, Table 10 demonstrates that the problem of resistance over threat of high taxes was greatest in the civil government projects of the Southeast, next extensive in the voluntary projects of the Southeast, and least extensive in the Northeast projects. Little differences were noted on such problems as those encountered with professionals, medical doctors, and influential persons.

The civil government projects of the Southeast employed to the smallest degree such media as news articles, speeches to organized groups, radio talks, and motion pictures. Voluntary hospital projects of the Southeast were inter-

Table 10

ORGANIZATIONAL PROBLEMS IN THE CIVIL GOVERNMENT AND VOLUNTARY
HOSPITAL PROJECTS IN THE SOUTHEAST COMPARED WITH THE NORTHEAST

Organizational Problem	Southeast		Northeast
	Civil Government	Voluntary	All Projects
	Percent	Percent	Percent
Threat of high taxes	67	47	21
Opposition of professionals (non-physicians)	—	6	4
Opposition of medical doctors	16	18	17
Total number of Projects	18	34	24

mediate in the use of such media as contrasted with all of the projects in the Northeast. The Northeast projects reported the extensive use of communication media. Surprisingly, the civil government projects of the Southeast surpassed the voluntary type of the Southeast in using personal contact, house bills, and posters. Again, it is necessary to note that the voluntary projects of the Southeast were intermediate to the other two groupings.

Table 11

COMMUNICATION MEDIA EMPLOYED BY THE CIVIL GOVERNMENT AND
VOLUNTARY HOSPITAL PROJECTS IN THE SOUTHEAST
COMPARED WITH THE NORTHEAST

Communication Media	Southeast		Northeast
	Civil Government	Voluntary	All Projects
	Percent	Percent	Percent
News articles	67	79	92
Personal contact	67	62	96
Speeches to organized groups	33	56	92
House bills and posters	28	18	29
Radio talks	17	24	25
Motion pictures	--	9	13
Total number of Projects	18	34	24

The Regional Profile

THIS chapter has noted briefly some regularities in the task of hospital acquisition as they are related to six major regions of the United States. The contrast of regional groupings of projects began at the point of the choice of sponsor for the hospital. The major finding was that the incidence of projects associated with local civil government varied within the regional classifications. Conversely, the incidence of projects possessing voluntary features likewise varied within the regional classifications.

Once the nexus of sponsorship was located, there followed related similarities and dissimilarities in community organization styles. As the incidence of civil government projects increased, the problems encountered decreased, the use of media and appeals to the community was less frequent, but success after one campaign increased. Voluntary projects provided a reciprocal profile. The important question raised by the civil government and voluntary profiles is to determine the extent to which prescribed official authority was the major capacity in the decision-making process.

The broad outlines of the successful attempts of small communities to acquire hospitals have been sketched. Previous chapters set forth the community organizational settings in which the labors of local people resulted in the erection of a new hospital. But the real part of the small hospital story was that which stood back of the outlines and community organizational settings. The remainder of the present study is a description of the events in five hospital communities, each of which was selected to represent the pattern of hospital acquisition in a specific region of the United States.

v. SOUTHEAST

As IT DOES in every community, the task of building a hospital in Southeast County had a particular history, which is one part of the story. This history really began in the early months of 1945 amidst spring plans for cotton and cattle, when the directors of the Southeast County Farm Bureau first discussed the need to improve hospital facilities. They had learned of impending federal legislation to promote hospital construction, and they also were aware of local discussions about the relationship between modern hospital facilities and attracting and maintaining physicians. But it was not until March, 1946 that the Farm Bureau directors met with the probate judge to arrange a public hearing on the advisability of proceeding further on a hospital project.

In April, 1946, this public hearing was called by the probate judge of Southeast County. The hearing was scheduled for the Court House. Among those in attendance were several professional leaders, school administrators, ministers, welfare workers, representatives of city councils for the two municipalities in the county, and the directors of the Farm Bureau. The net results of the hearing were approval of the project by those in attendance, and the appointment of 16 directors of a Southeast County Hospital Association by the probate judge. One director was to serve each of the 16 voting precincts, or beats, in Southeast County. The majority of the 16 directors were large landowners; three were the largest landowners in the county.

The executive committee of the Association, consisting of nine members, next circulated a petition to the voters of the county and obtained the signatures of 4,000 persons in favor of the hospital. The chairman of the executive committee, a large landowner and president of the Farm Bureau, presented the petition to the Commissioners Court. Consequently, in November, 1947, the Court approved a $60,000 bond issue in order to develop a facility in Carlin, the county seat, and one in Farmville, another small municipality, totaling 50 hospital beds. At this point some opposition was encountered. It was credited to two members of the Commissioners Court, representing a political faction in opposition to the probate judge, and a local physician who had formerly been a country practitioner in the northern hilly areas of Southeast County. Nevertheless, the public vote for the bond issue was passed by a two-thirds majority.

Then followed a surprise to the hospital sponsoring group. The intervening passage of Hill-Burton hospital legislation provided for federal assistance to the extent of one-third of construction costs. The directors of the local Hospital Association had believed previously that federal assistance would total two-thirds of the total cost. Two immediate decisions were made to counter-

57

act this unexpected obstacle to the financing of hospital construction. First, the Hospital Association reduced the size of the facility at Carlin to 21 beds, and dispensed with the proposed facility at Farmville. The second decision was to arrange for a local delegation to travel to the state capitol and petition for help from the state Building Commission. The probate judge arranged the appointment with the Building Commission. By this time the former probate judge, who had been in office when the project was initiated, had died and a new incumbent in political sympathy with the state administration had been appointed.

The state Building Commission agreed to contribute $50,000 of state funds, and later an additional $5,000, after a second session with the Commission. With these results, the construction of the hospital began. However, the increase of building costs and the substantial maintenance expenditures probable for the new hospital led the Southeast County executive committee of the Association to request the County Commissioners Court to levy a two-mill tax. This tax was to "be used solely for acquiring, constructing, operating, equipping, or maintaining county hospitals." With the hospital already under construction there seemed to be no alternative, as some informants put it, to approving this issue by public vote, which was done.

Simultaneous with the above events were the progress and delays of securing a site for the hospital. The original site for the hospital was owned by the Board of Education in the county seat of Carlin. However, this group became entangled in opposing political factions and decided to withhold the desired site. This event resulted in the appointment of a hospital site committee consisting almost entirely of the members of the Carlin City Council. The site committee finally arranged another location, which was duly donated by the city.

THE REGIONAL SETTING

THE visitor to Southeast County is struck by a quite obvious physical factor. Stretching diagonally from northeast to southwest across the county is a strip of prairie soil, bordered on the north and south by smooth to hilly uplands. The strip of soil is the famous Black Belt, the location of the plantation system and cotton culture.[1] Although the Black Belt continues to be the cotton-producing area of Southeast County, the shifting technological basis of agricultural enterprise is an added significant feature. After the cotton boll weevil attacked in 1914, the cotton economy was not only disrupted, but a new emphasis began toward the diversification of agricultural production. The familiar land cover of cotton gave way to grass and livestock.

Two municipalities provide the major focal points of business and trade. One is Carlin, the county seat, on the edge of the Black Belt. The other is Farmville, in the heart of the Black Belt. Carlin, with a population of just over 2,000, is the location of two small colleges, Broadview College and Carlin Military Academy. Farmville has a population of just under 2,000 and serves as the residence of several large landowners of Black Belt land. Nearby in another county is the city of Melba with a population of 20,000.

Negroes and Whites

ANOTHER readily observable fact of Southeast County is the disproportionate number of Negroes to whites. In the pre-Civil War period, rural population was centered in this and other Black Belt areas of the South. In 1940 Southeast County was 75 percent Negro, although since that date increasing numbers of Negroes have been involved in an out-migration. This migration was encouraged by a shift to grassland technology, with a resulting over-abundance of labor resources. Too, the decline of timber stands in the northern "hill country" has forced many white laborers and tenants to earn a living elsewhere, both in non-farm employment within the county and in metropolitan centers. With the change from cotton to grass, an increasing number of Negro farm workers purchased small tracts of land and became owner-operators. Nevertheless, the vast majority of Negroes are employed in the farming and ranching operations of the large landowners, or in the domestic service of their households. More than 75 percent of the farm units in Southeast County are operated by tenants under sharecropping arrangements, with Negro tenants outnumbering whites five to one.

The rich prairie lands of the Black Belt are the location of the large landowners, the highest rate of tenancy, and the highest rate of Negro tenancy. It is also the area possessing the greater number of Negro owner-operators. The "hill country" of north Southeast County never had a plantation history. There one finds small farm units, few large landowners, and the lowest rates of tenancy and Negro farm ownership.

Technological Change

ANOTHER observable phenomenon is the concentrated ownership of land in the Black Belt. Informants were agreed that some 30 owners control the bulk of the most fertile Black Belt land. One operator, with a heritage growing out of the plantation era, owns 27,000 acres. Others own land in amounts decreasing to 1,000–1,500 acres. These large landowners are quite aware of the shifting technology from cotton to grass. The innovations which this shift has required have been facilitated by the technical interests and training of the large landowners, with the assistance of subsidized aids offered by agricultural agencies. Some of the large owners reported that agricultural diversification had been retarded in many instances by the reluctance of Negro farm workers to change practices. This resistance was re-enforced by the ancestral relationship of many such workers to particular plantations, and the stated unwillingness of these operators to dislodge the workers in an insecure situation of over-abundant labor resources.[2]

Black Belt and Hill Country

STILL ANOTHER observable fact about Southeast County is that the Black Belt area still carries some of the tradition and most of the nostalgias of the plantation era. The families of the Black Belt believe that life on the land is in keeping with the heritage of the Old South and the challenges of the new. Black Belt people remind themselves that Southeast County affairs have long been felt in the life of the state.[3] The Black Belt people believe that the heritage of the South was one of land, and that the heritage is best held by the families who have remained on the prairie soils of the Black Belt.

The ownership of land is the basis of a social class system, especially when viewed from the vantage point of the big landowners. The owners control, as they always have, the life and times of Southeast County and have long exerted their influence in the affairs of the state. The economics of Carlin and Farmville depend on the holdings of the out-county people, especially those of the Black Belt. Many tradesmen and professionals are farm operators, while large landowners may reside in one of the two towns and manage their holdings in the hinterlands. Farmville has always been characterized by landowners living in town and traveling to holdings elsewhere. Carlin, as both a county-seat town and the site of two educational institutions, does not have this characteristic to the same extent.

Political Organization

In some ways the significant life of Southeast County is found in its political organization, for the "game" of Southeast County is to operate within and speculate about the resolving of political issues. The playing of the game occurs with a county-wide political organization freely known to the participants. Simple only in that it is solidly Democratic, the political organization of Southeast County is maintained through a set of formally constituted roles of authority upheld by an out-county informal political system with influence diffused through a relatively small number of large landowners and operators.

The most important axis upon which this organization turns is that of the County Commissioners Court. The Court consists of the probate judge and four county commissioners elected by the entire voting population. Each commissioner represents a different area of Southeast County. Tangent to the Court are other county offices which, although not apparently central, affect political behavior by meeting and deciding the problems of the area. These are the offices of tax collector, tax assessor, sheriff, and county clerk. The point of view toward the Commissioners Court, as well as the importance of political affairs, is quite uniform. Such statements were typical: "The probate judge is supposed to run the politics of the county," "Black Belt politics have developed the affairs of Alabama since the beginning." "The last place in the South where people know how to be politicians is in the Black Belt." [4]

A review of the hinterlands of Southeast County must focus around certain pivotal points. First, one finds a number of "communities" in Southeast County. Each "community" approximates a plantation holding of an earlier day, now the large landowner holding of the present. Each is populated by Negroes and whites who are tenants or who work on the large landed estates. The important focal point of these "plantation-bounded" communities is the social and economic institution of the store. Although somewhat less than formerly, the Southeast County rural store is a business venture of the large landowner. It forms a commissary for the economic and consumer wants of the workers on the estate, and provides the means whereby workers, both Negro and white, may obtain credit from the landowner while awaiting harvest and in periods of agricultural adversity. These complex credit arrangements, and the appointed times for "settlin' and advancing," provide one way for directing the political behavior of people residing in store-centered communities. In this way great numbers of people living on the land are related to the political organization through traditional credit systems.

The community organization of Southeast County and its attending political life form a kind of machinery. To this mechanism the holders of influence in the out-county store-centered communities may initiate, or be initiated by, the incumbents of formally constituted political offices. Informants reported: "At one time you only needed to know 20 men in Southeast County to get things across." The 20 men were actually large landowners in the Black Belt. Another informant said, "The store is where people talk about politics, cotton, and cattle." A former court commissioner noted, "When I was in office I was concerned with only about 20 men and never had to really make a campaign in the usual sense." The same commissioner said, "We want that class of people [certain Black Belt large landowners and storekeepers] to run the county."

Decision-Making Capacities

DECISION-MAKING in Southeast County has to do with two roles. One is the politically authoritative position of the probate judge and other members of the Commissioners Court; the other is the influence of the large landowner-storekeeper.

The capacity of influence of the large landowner-storekeeper is actually threefold. One aspect is positional. The other two aspects relate to specific social properties owned by the incumbent of the role. The positional aspect deals with family and kinship position. The important social properties are, first, a resource of respect that is concentrated on "education and refinement," or a "lack of being narrow," and, second, maximum access into the associational life of Southeast County. The associational life has been furthered more recently by county-wide special interest groups organized about land and its technologies.

The positional elements of family and kinship lead to a ranking of the big landowners and storekeepers of Southeast County on a continuum of "old family." Top ranking is given the "old family that came from South Carolina." An old family without this background may be referred to as "haven't got the background," or "kinda' in the middle." Contrasted sharply are the judgments about those who hail from the "hill country." The old family Black Belt landowner, one which has "the Black Belt tradition," does not believe that being "hill country" would prevent aspirations to high influence and position in Southeast County. Indeed, the present probate judge is a man of the hills. Before this is approved, however, the requirement of obtaining "refinement," and a decrease in the expected desire "to only make money," are both demanded. Coupled here is an extended kinship pattern, part of which has to do with the Black Belt, and part with the "hill country." In the case of one Black Belt family, six members operate country stores and manage large holdings of land. Two other Black Belt families are related by marriage and, between them, own the largest acreage in the county.

Tangential Associations

SEVERAL associations integrate the social life of Southeast County still further. They provide opportunities for interaction between entire segments of the county and serve to bring together the incumbents of political offices and the holders of influence.

Of great importance is the Farm Bureau. This county-wide organization draws a majority of its members from the Black Belt, and is large-owner-dominated insofar as officers and directors are concerned. The Farm Bureau in Southeast County has undergone a recent rapid growth, and throughout a ten-year period an examination of recurring officers and directors demonstrates that the leading and large landowners, doubling as store owners, have been in charge. The second out-county association offering the same sort of tangency as the Farm Bureau is the Cattlemen's Association which, in some ways, is a symbol of the new day of cattle and grassland farming. Officerships in the Farm Bureau and Cattlemen's Association are frequently overlapping. In addition to these two major county-wide associations are found a variety of special interest groups, which often have developed around "the sporting world." Recruiting largely from the large landowner group, these associations are devoted to such interests as "fox hunting dogs," "Tennessee Walking Horses," and "Aberdeen Angus competition."

The county-wide associations, organized around the new economy of cattle and grass, provide a tangency in which political officials and the holders of out-county influence are associated for other than political purposes. This tangency provides not only an operational arena in Southeast County but also a means whereby alignments and re-alignments may organize the resources of Southeast County for the solution of county problems.

Few such solutions, however, escape the current "political faction." [5] The faction may be but two or three persons who, through differences on political issues, attempt to negotiate for the resources of the Southeast County political system. The faction stimulates transferrals, movements, and exchanges of social property vested in the entire county; and makes possible the manipulation of authority, influence, kinship, prestiged positions, and the flexibilities of associational life.

One very real property owned by those with authority and influence is that of votes. The roles of political office and land ownership prescribe the possession of a quantity of votes which may be exchanged, negotiated for, or used in bargaining for advantage in the strategies which are required. In addition, inward-facing and outward-facing accessibility provide another form of property which enters into the exchanges and bargainings of the system.

Hence, in the hospital project, the state political affiliation of the probate judge was a necessary resource.[6]

The sum of this is that knowledge of time-worn political arrangements in Southeast County is crucial to an understanding of how non-political issues are resolved. Decision-making in Southeast County has for its scope the entire county, and the above analysis has accented only the importance of the out-county organization, especially as it is concerned with the large landowners and storekeepers of the Black Belt. In addition, the towns of Carlin and Farmville must be included, since they constitute islands of decision-making which are not crucial in the over-all initiation of action, but which must be reckoned with for the votes which they possess.

Carlin and Farmville

IN Farmville, the city council is composed of landowners who reside in the town, and at least one "old family that came from South Carolina" has passed a membership on Farmville's city council through several generations. In Carlin, members of the city council are not representatives of the large land-owner group, but are engaged in business. The male heads of five families have membership on the city council, and have developed certain male civic organizations such as a Junior Chamber of Commerce and, more recently, a Lions Club. Less than ten families control the leadership of the social, recreational, and civic clubs of Carlin.

Two prevailing interests of Carlin families are Broadview College and Carlin Military Academy. One of Carlin's important persons is the retired superintendent of the Academy. Today his son serves in that position. Another Carlin civic leader has served for years as a trustee of Broadview College, continually active during this time in large fund-raising campaigns for the College. This same person stated: "It is true that we have a small town, but we enjoy the contact of educated and traveled people, and the opportunity to enjoy the good artists that the College attracts." Throughout the years there have been threats to move Broadview College to a more lucrative location. Each time the move was resisted by Carlin people, and Broadview College continues as a cherished tradition of the town. People point with pride to the College as the oldest one of its kind in the South. Thus, the life of Carlin is, in one sense, the life of Broadview and "CA," the vernacular reference made to the military academy. Beyond this, much of the daily routine of living in Carlin revolves around the busy schedules of four churches, Baptist, Methodist, Presbyterian, and Episcopal. The predominant church in size and activity is the Baptist. One of Carlin's city councilmen pointed to this church and reviewed the historical agreements that had been reached within its walls, which affected, as he said, the affairs of early education and religion in Alabama. Carlin informants generally believed that the "ways of the world" were less associated with Carlin than with Farmville, "where people stop work at four and start drinking for the rest of the evening."

Carlin is linked to the life of Southeast County by the blood kinship that extends through town and country alike, by the membership of town dwellers

63

in such organizations as the Farm Bureau, by its advantageous communicative position as the county seat, and, importantly, by the business dependence of the town dwellers on the operations of the large landowners.

Farmville is even more directly a part of life in the Black Belt. Farmville, the home of generations of cotton planters, is a center of business and residence for several large landowners of a rich portion of Black Belt land. Until recently, a prominent landowner was a member of the County Commissioners Court.

The distinction between the two municipalities of Carlin and Farmville is that Farmville is incorporated into the entire county organization for purposes of decision-making, while Carlin, more autonomous, is only recurrently courted for the solution of county problems because of the block of votes which it contains. The manipulation of Carlin is currently more difficult than formerly, when a highly favored probate judge was a Carlin man. Today, the probate judge is an out-county man, not to mention his background in the northern hill country.[7] Farmville informants hold Carlin under suspicion of being unprogressive. As one informant said, Carlin was "just a necessary evil." Also recurrently mentioned is the belief that the city fathers of Carlin are content with the traditions of its two institutions of learning and, in a desire to maintain a "peaceful life," have resisted the coming of new business pursuits. One informant stated that the people of Carlin were afraid that the approach of new industry would mean that "The Jews would own it, the Gentiles would run it, and the niggers would enjoy it."

MAKING DECISIONS AND GAINING APPROVAL

INITIATING THE PROJECT. The history of getting a hospital in Southeast County was a succession of four important decisions. The first decision was to initiate the project. Actually, the idea of a new hospital in Southeast County depended on three circumstances. One circumstance was the rapid growth of the county Farm Bureau and a consequent attention to hospitalization insurance. Another was the early familiarity with impending federal legislation to assist local hospital construction. The third circumstance was an increase in the feeling of need by county residents, encouraged by the acceptance of hospitalization insurance but without proper hospital facilities.

The very thought of a hospital immediately provoked a mixed public reaction. Such a project would limit the expenditures of public funds for a favored interest, the development and maintenance of rural roads. Too, the project would place an added burden on the chief taxpayers of the county, the 30 or more large landowners in the Black Belt. There were still other groups involved in making the initiatory decision. The first was the Farm Bureau board of directors, with the president who first proposed the plan. The second was the Court of County Commissioners with the probate judge, who could legitimately make the decision. The third element was the large landowner group who, by recogizing the consequences that would disproportionately accrue to them could, with a positional and influential control of the out-county political system, approve or disapprove the entire proposal. Accordingly, the fundamental problem of starting the project in Southeast County was that of acquiring the cooperation, or neutralizing the influence, of the large landowners in the Black Belt. How this was done is the heart of the story of getting a new hospital in Southeast County.

The first negotiation of record is that between the president of the Farm Bureau and the County Commissioners Court. The physicians of the county were invited to the original parley. At this first meeting the representatives of the Farm Bureau made no mention of a possible bond issue to provide Southeast's share of construction costs. Instead, the strategy of carrying the Court included the tactic of explaining that the Farm Bureau would underwrite the local costs, variously estimated from $25,000 to $40,000. That the tactic was successful is proven by the suggestion of the Court that a public hearing be

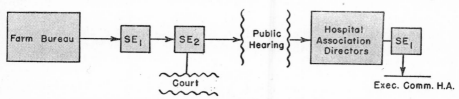

FIGURE 6. Southeast County Pattern of Initial Negotiations

called to explore the matter and to ascertain the public sentiment. As members of the Court reported, the real problem was not one of finance but of bringing the large landowners "into the open." Thus, it would be possible to predict potential opposition to the project on the part of landowners and certain political factions, and especially to see if the large landowners would support the hospital "as individuals and outside the Farm Bureau."

So it came about that the public hearing was conducted. In attendance at the Court House meeting were members of the Commissioners Court, Farm Bureau directors, several large landowners, physicians, and delegates of health, educational, and welfare agencies. The issue of this meeting, apart from gaining support for the project, was to form an official planning and operating body for the hospital. This procedure was prescribed by legislation for compliance in the receipt of federal funds. During the hearing the concern of both the Court and the Farm Bureau directors was that of officially committing the landowner-storekeepers to the project.

Consequently the probate judge appointed a board of 16 directors for a Southeast County Hospital Association. The list of appointees was submitted by the Farm Bureau and included the more prominent large landowners of the Black Belt. By this procedure the strategies of both the Court and the Farm Bureau were fulfilled. The alliance was further secured, moreover, by publishing the names of the 16 Hospital Association directors in the Southeast County weekly paper in order publicly to identify the Black Belt landowners with the proposed project.

The immediate reactions of the landowners were varied. Several admitted that they were individually opposed to the project, but that the promotion tactics had been successful in forcing them to "go along with the project." As they pointed out, their reputations of "education and refinement" as traditional Black Belt representatives made it impossible to resist the obviously good implications of a new hospital. In addition, the landowners doubted that the project would succeed, and thus, little would be lost. A few depended on the belief that the Court itself had merely performed the ritual of listening to public interest, and would subsequently delay further action toward a new hospital.

Raising Funds

HOWEVER, the newly initiated project in Southeast County was not delayed, largely because everyone was committed to everyone else. In addition, the original probate judge had died and the new incumbent proved to be in sympathy with the state administration and the "hill country," but out of favor with the landowners of the Black Belt. Although the Farm Bureau and the landowners, by means of the Hospital Association, were in charge of operations on the project, the Court was still the official sponsor. Notwithstanding the original promise of the Farm Bureau to underwrite the project locally, the probate judge finally put to vote a bond issue of $60,000. Certain events had occurred to obscure the original promise made by the Farm Bureau. In addition to the advent of a new probate judge, new federal legislation was passed that promised to supply less of the construction costs than was earlier expected and resistance developed to the project from a political faction strongly opposed to the incumbent state administration and the probate judge.

The bond issue for the new hospital, replacing fulfillment of the promise of the Farm Bureau, suggests a strengthening of the new probate judge's administration, especially in the "hill country" where the opposing political faction was entrenched. Too, with the change in political climate, the bond issue provided a way for the Farm Bureau to work with the Court and yet remain free of publicly construed "deals" with it. While the probate judge favored the bond issue, the other commissioners did not. Recognizing this, the directors of the Farm Bureau circulated a petition to gain an indication of support from the people, and subsequently provided 4,000 names of taxpayers to the probate judge. Such a testimonial led the Court to approve putting to a vote a bond issue of $60,000, which was passed by a two-thirds majority.

Organizing the Sponsoring Group

ALTHOUGH the sponsoring organization was visible at the time of earliest initiation, certain subleties of this process should be emphasized. The County Commissioners Court was the official sponsor. Yet, this function was extended to others, making possible the neutralization of the resources and proficiencies of others, especially the landowners of the Black Belt. In Southeast County the initiating decisions were made by decision-makers with the authority of constituted civil offices. Yet, these persons recognized that certain other re-

66

sources and proficiencies rested with the influential landowners, i. e., wealth, respect, and access. Since strategy may be defined as the attempt to gain or to neutralize the resources and proficiencies possessed by others, mere attendance by the landowners at the public hearing was not enough. Instead, the resources and proficiencies of the landowners had to be "moved over" from the out-county system to a firmly aligned relationship with the Court and the Farm Bureau.

It is significant that after the appointment of the Hospital Association directors, the total Association group became inactive. The executive committee, composed of the original initiating directors of the Farm Bureau, assumed the details of operations. By these devices, the directors of the Farm Bureau became officially and legitimately incorporated, but not as representatives of the Farm Bureau, into the active sponsoring function. Likewise, the locus of rightful decision-making, or legitimacy, moved in and through agencies of civil authority.

Countering Rising Costs

BEYOND the exigencies of initiation and sponsorship was always the shadow of insufficient dollars. This was as true in Southeast County as it was in all the other cases. Since fund-raising by any method required a period of time, original estimations of construction costs were found wanting at the close of a fund-raising period. This was due to the interim effects of steadily increasing building costs. Resolving this difficulty made up a major class of necessary decisions.

In Southeast County the expectation had been that the federal government would supply two-thirds of the construction costs. The eventual ratio was one-third of the total cost. Expecting the two-thirds figure, the original bond issue of $60,000 had passed by a public vote. Two decisions were made to offset this damage—the Farmville health center was eliminated from the project, and the size of the Carlin facility was reduced from 50 to 20 beds. Since Farmville was in the middle of the Black Belt, one might expect that such a decision would permanently alienate the landowners of that area. However, it did not. The reason was simply that the large landowners saw the emasculation of the Farmville facility as the beginning of the eventual failure of the entire project, to many a most welcome event. Next, the political identification of the probate judge with the locally opposed state administration provided the needed access to negotiate two contributions from the state Building Commission.

The third and final decision to alleviate unanticipated building costs was to place before the public a two-mill sales tax for the purpose, not only of completing the hospital construction but, for a brief period, to provide public support for operation. That this was passed favorably by public vote was explained locally by its introduction after construction was under way. The alternative of a partially completed and deteriorating building provided an easy rationalization for voting positively for the sales tax.

THE OVER-VIEW

THE GAME of Southeast County was, and is today, politics. The solution to problems of respectable magnitude occurs, as it always has, amidst the swirls and currents of "factions," "deals," "maneuvers," and playing chess with votes. Getting a hospital in Southeast County was not a parade of meetings, of education, of extensive appeals, or of appropriate publicity. It was, instead, a struggle of commitment, with the rules of the struggle freely known but never stated. A great number of "those who counted" in Southeast County saw the hospital as the road to a perennial county debt. Since those who counted pay the taxes, the modern facility overlooking the county seat of Carlin still seems to many people a kind of modern miracle. Yet, it happened. Here was a case of community organization in which the goal of the majority was reached in spite of opposition from the powerful groups involved. That this could happen is the drama of Southeast County.

The drama itself was acted on a stage of tradition and status, history and nostalgia, and of southern honor. To live one's life in the Black Belt of Southeast County is to live in accordance with the code of "the old family from South Carolina." It also means supervising the holdings of land, cotton, and cattle; running the store; and negotiating with the votes of the men and women who buy, discuss, and obtain credit in the plantation store. No small part of the drama is concerned with that body of rights which go with the reins of civil government. The probate judge is astride the connections between town and country, between Black Belt and "hill country," between white and Negro, and between county and state.

Life in Southeast County is the very epitome of order. Whether one joins the old men who sit the hours away on the Court House lawn, manages the 300 workers on the estate, sells oil to the planters, or attends a lecture at Broadview, he will find the pattern of life in Southeast County. The rules insist that big problems are county problems. There was never a question that a new hospital was other than a county hosptial. Once so defined, the rules produced the "triple play" of Southeast County—the Court, the Black Belt, and the "hill country." Acquiring a hospital was a problem of moving an idea from the out-county into, and perhaps through, the Court. As it so often happens, the process of moving through the Court picks up, on the way, the embracing figure of the probate judge. Then the problem becomes one of aligning the "pros and the cons" to establish favor for the idea. The way to do it is to gain the word of the landowner, and, at the same time, his votes and his ability to bear the burden of taxes. Without this one is left to the "hill country," and the delicate balance of hill country factions makes this recourse far from predictable. Of course, both the Black Belt and the "hill country" can agree, and then the old men on the Court House lawn will whisper of deals and trades and promises. Yet, as they say in Southeast County, the probate judge will know before the old men. He is in the middle, for he is the logistical expert on exchanges, withdrawals, and transfer of votes, on promises, resources, and proficiencies.

Thus, in Southeast County the initiation of the hospital idea was a problem of sponsorship. The rules suggested that a county organization of both civil officials and landowners, the Farm Bureau, should be the locus of initiation. The organization of sponsorship was also the securing of a commitment, not of interest or enthusiasm, but a commitment on the basis of history, tradition, and honor. Then followed the problems of finding enough dollars, using the legal instrumentalities of the Court, official channels to the state capitol, and capitalizing on political debt between county and state. Finally, the one-time officials of the Farm Bureau who had initiated the idea found themselves official agents of the Court, supported by the public commitments of the Black Belt. From there it was a matter of contracts, architects, bricks, sites, and an increasing concern over what would happen when the hospital was built.

Yet, change is accelerating in Southeast County, and not only of cotton to grass, nor of tenant to owner. One must wonder about the future of the old system when the plantation store no longer serves as the center of "advancin' and settlin' ". In fact, it hardly does today. What will become of the old nostalgias when Carlin gets a new factory, new people, new executives, new notions of community endeavor, and a reluctance to continue as an island in the swirls of political maneuvering in Southeast County? Will there then be a Commissioners Court and its probate judge, as the capstone of a hierarchy, still encountering the "deals" in the hills and the prairies of its domain?

VI. MIDSTATE

THROUGHOUT World War II the citizens of Larch, the county seat of Midstate County, had been concerned about the 30 miles of driving required by a respected local physician to reach modern hospital facilities. Local doctors found it necessary to refer all patients to a metropolitan hospital some 30 miles distant. The long winter months, said local people, made hazardous driving for doctors, and the time required for hospital calls reduced the hours available for office duty. Still no visible event had occurred to demonstrate that a hospital was in the making.

In March, 1945, a weekly newspaper in Larch initiated a series of articles about the need for a hospital in Midstate County. They summarized impending federal legislation to provide assistance to local hospital projects. They quoted similar articles and accounts of accomplishment from other journals and newspapers. These accounts continued from March through November of 1945. As a climax to this series, the editor of the Larch newspaper organized a "Sunday morning breakfast" in November. Physicians of Midstate County, a variety of businessmen, and two prominent industrialists came. At this early morning meeting, recommendations were made to initiate a project to build a hospital in Larch, and to attempt a voluntary subscription of funds which the newspaper editor believed would provide necessary construction costs.

An attempt was made to raise funds by public subscription immediately after this meeting. The attempts were, however, not organized, and the result was a few hundred dollars collected, largely through the contributions of two local organizations. This encouraged the belief that voluntary public subscription for funds would not be successful and that more formal instrumentalities would be necessary. In the spring of 1946 a hearing was held at the Larch Court House, at which the circuit judge read to the attending taxpayers the legal provisions for developing a hospital by a voted bond issue. A temporary hospital committee developed from this meeting, with two persons charged with active promotional work. These men were new to the community, one an official of a Larch chain store, the other a chiropodist and a son-in-law of the circuit judge.

Public notice of determination to issue bonds was released in November, 1946. Prior to this event, promotional meetings were conducted in the county. A necessary step in the issuance of bonds was that a petition be signed by at least 200 taxpayers, indicating a willingness to submit the bond issue to public vote. This was accomplished in the summer of 1946 and the petition was submitted to the Board of Commissioners in September of that year. The public vote in November, 1946, resulted in passage, although considerable resistance was manifested by the voters in and about the town of Westville, a municipality on the west side of Midstate County. Throughout the county, the vote was 2 to 1 in favor of the bond issue, but in the voting precinct including Westville, the vote was 3 to 1 against. In the series of routine events, following the election, the most important was the appointment of a hospital board of five members by the Board of Commissioners. Considered rapidly thereafter by the board were such questions as the investigation of architect firms, building plans, state regulations, federal assistance, and site location.

During the winter of 1946-47, the editor of the Larch weekly newspaper began again to refer to the hospital project. He stated that it was his purpose, and that of the newspaper, to guarantee that the people would know all the facts about the hospital development. In making public the deliberations of the hospital board, exposures were made in the paper of an alleged irregularity in the handling of finance by the Hospital Board. This was one factor in the eventual resignation of the two active promoters mentioned earlier, one of whom had become chairman of the Hospital Board, the other appointed "tentatively" as the proposed hospital administrator. In addition, difficulties of the two promotional workers increased when disagreements occurred over payment for their services. Their resignations were submitted and reappointments were made. This time four of the board members were from the town of Larch and one from Westville.

In April, 1948, property owners filed a petition to request the issuance of bonds by the county in an amount not exceeding $200,000 for the purpose of providing funds for constructing and equipping a county hospital. Within a few days, however, a remonstrance was filed against the sale of bonds. This was a petition with more signers than the original petition in favor of the bond issuance, and concentrated on the "west side" of Midstate County. The basis of this remonstrance was that the legal wording of the original petition and ballot in regard to the bond issue was legally incorrect in terms of mandating the Board of Commissioners to sell the bonds.

After the appropriate state tax authorities had supported the legality of the remonstrance, a delay continued until early 1949. During the intervening period, federal assistance became available to the extent of $100,000. By this time, three members of the seven-man Hospital Board were medical doctors from Larch, three were Larch businessmen, and one was a wealthy landowner from Westville. The hospital board broke the impasse by encouraging the filing of petitions by groups within the county in order to remove the delaying action of the remonstrance. As a result, a legal hearing was called in April, 1949. The remonstrance was declared "unverified" by a visiting judge, and its delaying action was removed.

From this point, the Midstate County hospital project progressed through solution of the technical details for construction, the acceptance of bids from architects, further negotiations with federal authorities, and the sale of bonds. By late 1949, federal regulations were amended to permit dollar for dollar matching with federal funds. The proposed hospital was now valued at more than $400,000. Construction began in the latter part of 1950, with official opening scheduled for 1951.

THE PROJECT SETTING

MIDSTATE County is an area of suburbanization and commercialization. This was not always true, for Midstate County, settled in 1850, was long retarded in development because of the excessively swampy condition of its terrain. The application of modern technology provided drainage and reclamation, and allowed development of productive vegetable gardening on the fertile muck lands. With the increase in commercial agriculture, the proximity of Midstate County to adjacent cities occasioned an influx of workers to small parcels of land and a resulting growth in numbers of commuting workers to nearby industrial plants. These workers have included great numbers of people from the southern Piedmont areas. As one informant stated, "The Kentuckians have taken over Indiana without firing a shot." Another major trend has been the development of a recreational and resort industry about the lakes of the county.

The physical characteristics of Midstate County lead to division into two distinct areas referred to locally as the "east side" and the "west side." The eastern half of the county is subdivided into small farms practicing general agriculture, and into the small plots of city workers. On the western side of the county occurs the preponderance of muck land and the greatest development of commercial vegetable gardening. One of the repeated references to the west side of Midstate County is an account of two brothers who started on a small farm 15 years ago, initiating a vegetable gardening enterprise with horses. Today it is reported that the extensive gardening operations of the brothers involve 75 tractors in constant operation.

For the "east side" of Midstate County, the trade and service center is the county seat of Larch. Larch had a 1940 population of 2,500, presently almost doubled because of the in-migration that occurred during and since World War II. Larch is a center of Republican politics. Its population is chiefly of old American stock, with a considerable number of suburban dwellers who had migrated from Kentucky and other states during the War years. For the "west side" of Midstate County, the trade and service center is the town of Westville, with a population of 2,700. Informants reported that this town serves as the center of Democratic politics, and is populated by mixed European stock. References were frequently heard to Westville as "Little Europe." It is predominantly Catholic, as is its surrounding trade area. Larch, on the other hand, is predominantly a Protestant town. Westville has well-developed industrial activity, with a garment factory and a special ornament processing plant. Larch is more commercial with indigenous small businesses, although a small war industry was organized there in the early years of the war, which attracted the southern workers.

Old Americans and Newcomers

BOTH THE wealth and the organized associational life of Midstate County are concentrated in the two municipalities of Larch and Westville. Even the commercial farmers of the "west side" are a part of the civic and religious life of Westville. A crude differentiation of the class and status systems of the county would be a dichotomy of the "old Americans," construed locally as Anglo-Saxon stock of some residence in the county, but not necessarily "old family" in the sense of pioneer settlement; and the multiplicity of other ethnic groups, predominantly middle European. Especially in Westville one finds increasing numbers of Mexicans, recruited to assist the commercial gardening enterprises. Finally, there are the "K-Y's," the in-migrants of the past few years from the South, especially the Piedmont area. Informants pointed out that in an earlier period the "Kentuckians" would come for seasonal labor duties, and then return to their homeland for the winter. Local people believe now that once a "Kentuckian" arrives, he is in Midstate County to stay. One informant pointed out that after World War II such in-migrants for seasonal labor would not follow the earlier practice of being taken home by their employer after the season was over, and cited the case of one farmer who "loaded up a bunch (of Kentuckians) and took them back to Kentucky, but they all beat him back to Midstate County."

Both Larch and Westville have their elite groups, locally referred to as "crowds." Thus, one "crowd" may organize around frequent visiting at the homes of each member and, in the case of Larch, make frequent trips to nearby metropolitan centers for attendance at the theatre, night-clubbing, and expensive dining. Such "crowds" in Westville appear to be less mobile and relate more to church functions and local civic organizations. In the elite group of Westville one finds certain wealthy businessmen, the industrialists, and the large commercial gardeners. All the evidence points to the exclusiveness of such "crowds" or elite groups both in Larch and Westville. A few informants from the elite speak of a "middle bunch," "who work hard to get some place, but don't know very much." Included here would be the bulk of the small businessmen, the general and subsistence farmers, and the paid professionals. Medical doctors and lawyers are considered to be among the elite, especially in the county seat of Larch.

The influence of ethnics is uncertain. The lower-income representatives of European ancestry appear to rank somewhat higher in Westville than in Larch, since this ethnic concentration in and around Westville has produced some prominent representatives in business and industry. The valuations made in Larch place them lower. Mexicans, poor Kentuckians, and old American "welfare cases" tend to lump into a lower class. The Mexicans and "K-Y's" compete for lowest place.

Urbanization

PERHAPS the single most important characteristic that impresses the observer is the rapid change which occurred in the past ten years in Midstate County. This has to do with the in-migration of southern farm workers and the ethnic groups of Westville. Not only have Larch and Westville increased in population with these migrants, but the familiar symptoms of suburbanization are

73

found at their fringes. Also impressive are the advantageous results of commercialized farming to some operators, and its shifting of these same operators from a position of an "open-country subsistence farmer" to a position of businessman in the town circles and "crowds" of Larch and Westville. The most casual observer would not overlook the relation of Midstate County to the orbits of surrounding metropolitan centers, and the extent of the relationship is indicated by the mobility of county residents to and from these centers for purposes of employment, economic services, and the arts.

Poverty and Public Affairs

PRACTICALLY all of the informants encountered in Midstate County referred directly or indirectly to their homeland of Midstate County as "a very poor county." Actually, there occur a variety of themes which appear prevalent in discussions of public affairs. Among them are property, taxes, economy in government, and sound business management. The beliefs of most informants about the poverty of the county are not borne out by county statistics. The level of living index for Midstate County is only slightly below the average for the entire state. Much concern was evidenced over the "rights of the individual" and "high taxes and property holders." Higher taxes to support public projects would seem to be one of the constant fears of Midstate people. Taxes are held to be not only very real burdens in "a poor county," but symbols of interference with the rights of the citizen.

Political Organization

THE ORIENTATION of the Midstate hospital project to the jurisdiction of the county relates to the relevance of the entire county as the setting for the solution of major problems. The evidence suggests that the only county-wide formal organization for the solution of major problems is that of the county political organization. No association has an important county focus. Associations are primarily organized in the interests of the "communities" of Larch and Westville. Certain county-wide rural organizations are present, together with a beginning associational development in the new resort community of Valley Lake.

Political affairs take place largely within the Board of County Commissioners, made up of a representative from each of the townships. One of the important committees of this group is the county council, which is charged with many financial decisions. Related to the Board of Commissioners is a series of political positions, which generally affect the conduct of county affairs and which, specifically, relate to the hospital project. These are the offices of county auditor, county treasurer, and, to a lesser extent, the sheriff. The office of probate judge contrasts sharply with the same office in Southeast County. In Midstate County the probate judge does not occupy a superordinate position with the Board of Commissioners, but devotes considerable time to the administration of welfare activities. Perhaps the most influential political position in Midstate County is that of the circuit judge, who presides at jury trials but functions also as a source of legal knowledge.

Although politics is reported to be important in Midstate County, political events are not a "game" as in Southeast County. Being a member of a political party is important in choosing participation in certain networks of social relationships, yet political activity lodges in the county seat with the largely perfunctory duties of the Board of Commissioners. Informants in Midstate County emphasize the "ability to be neutral." County projects, such as hospitals, are construed to be "out of the realm of politics." Thus, political organization is seen in two ways: as a means to handle the affairs of county business, and as an arrangement to resolve problems that are "not political." The members of the county political organization and their paraphernalia, "the court room," are supposed to remain neutral.

County political organization divides somewhat equally along party lines and centers in the towns of Larch and Westville. Larch serves as a Republican stronghold, and the town of Westville is the Democratic center. Weekly newspapers provide the organs whereby party positions are kept alive and communicated.

Actually, Midstate County is two counties in one. The "east side" is centered in the county seat of Larch, and the "west side" in the smaller industrial Westville. In addition to political differences, the towns of Larch and Westville are reported to have a historic rivalry. Numerous incidents were reported, such as the Westville report that "Larch had stolen the best basketball coach we ever had." The questionnaire returned from Midstate stated: "Opposition came from another town because its citizens opposed the hospital being located at Larch, believing that the county-seat town would gain more business." The evidence would support the conclusion that the communication between the two towns was poorly developed. Several informants on the "west side" did not know some of the persons in Larch who were active on the Hospital Board and, indeed, the chairman of the board, a Larch businessman, was not known to several. This characteristic differs from that of Southeast, since in the latter situation participants in the political organization were well aware of the way in which the organization functions, and even those outside "played the game" in terms of alignments over issues.

Informants in each case study were asked: "As applied locally, what do you mean by the word, community?" Nine out of 10 respondents in Midstate County agreed that the town and its service area was the important grouping reserved for the name of community. Of growing importance is the resort community of Valley Lake, placed midway between Larch and Westville. In the hospital project and in other ways, Valley Lake increasingly serves to mediate the rivalry between the two older centers.

Both Larch and Westville exhibit the usual associational pattern of the small town, with male service clubs being recommended by informants as the "way to get things started." Of particular importance are the Chamber of Commerce in Westville and the Rotary Club in Larch. To these associations belong the businessmen of each town, the industrialists of Westville, and the self-employed professionals of Larch such as physicians and lawyers. Since Larch has more practicing physicians, the County Medical Society has its organizational focus there.

Each town has a town council for immediate handling of public matters that pertain to the respective municipalities. In regard to the hospital project, the town councils as total groups did not play a part. One specific opposition to the hospital project stemmed from a member of the Larch town council, but as an individual rather than a representative of the council.

Tangent Associations

THERE is no single Midstate association, such as the Farm Bureau in Southeast County, which meshes with the county political structure, or provides either a form of integration or an arena in which both incumbents of authority and influence may be joined for community or county problem-solving. Articulation within the towns of Westville and Larch occurs by means of the Chamber of Commerce in the former and the Rotary Club in the latter. The Farm Bureau is a prominent organization in the out-county rural areas, but lacks tangency with the town of Larch, especially, and is tangent in Westville only to the extent that a few wealthy commercial gardeners on the "west side" belong to both the Farm Bureau and the local Chamber of Commerce. Not a single association was pointed out by Midstate County informants as being the continuing sponsor of projects that concern the entire county. Indeed, the associational complex would seem to pivot about the towns, with an enlarging scope in Westville relating to the commercialization of agriculture on the "west side" and the subsequent introduction of farmers into associational and religious activities.

The County Medical Society had a particular relevance to the hospital project. It is doubtful whether the Medical Society would provide a continuing associational framework for the introduction and sponsorship of other county projects. However, the Medical Society was quite relevant to the specific issue of the hospital as the only organized expression of the medical or allied health professions in the county.

MAKING DECISIONS AND GAINING APPROVAL

THE BEGINNING of the hospital project in Midstate County was actually the campaign of one man, the publisher and editor of the Larch weekly newspaper. The editor, new to Midstate County, was aware of impending federal legislation regarding hospital construction. He knew, also, of certain successful experiences of other localities with voluntary subscription of funds. His series of newspaper editorial articles served to elicit letters and testimonials from the citizens of Midstate County which made the hospital possibility a public issue. The articles stimulated recommendations from men in military service and brought up the advisability of a "memorial" hospital. They served to remind residents of the county that certain disadvantageous health conditions were present. After an article dealt with a count of recent deaths of mothers during childbirth, the Board of County Commissioners recommended that action was needed to improve Midstate County's hospital facilities. The Board suggested the alternative of improving the facilities of the Midstate County Home. This event encouraged the editor to proceed beyond the series of editorials.

The "Sunday morning breakfast" brought forth the important initiating decision. The avowed purpose of the meeting was to explore informally the possibility of a new hospital for Midstate County, as well as the appropriate methods of financing one. Among those present were the physicians of the county, the Circuit Judge, a few businessmen and leaders of associations from Larch, two industrialists, and the editors of both party papers in Larch. The editor of the Republican paper was the author of the previous editorial series; and the other was referred to as the "wheelhorse" for the Democratic Party in the county.

As believed by those present at the "Sunday morning breakfast," the major strategy involved was that of gaining approval for a voluntary public subscription of funds for hospital purposes, to be organized and led by the editor of the newspaper which had initiated the series of editorials. If this was the intended strategy, it failed completely. A major conflict began which was to carry throughout the project, explaining much of the difficulty and delay which the Midstate project was to encounter. The disagreement was based not on the feasibility of building a new hospital, but on the possibilities of a voluntary subscription. The two industrialists joined with the editor, who was suggesting it as the correct method of raising funds. One stated that "he would top the highest contribution made." The others at the meeting believed that a legal instrumentality should be employed. This view was sponsored by the circuit judge, reportedly on the grounds that the incumbent Republican administration in the county could well be associated with a new hospital. The editor of the Democratic paper also supported the legal instrumentality, reportedly because of rivalry with the other initiating editor and his desire to force the Republican administration of the county into a formal taxing of the people.

Physicians present at the meeting reported that they personally had preferred the voluntary subscription, but agreed with the adherents of the legal instrumentalities because this method would insure a county hospital, which they believed to be a more realistic plan than a hospital based exclusively on the service area of Larch.

Two committees were formed during the "Sunday morning breakfast." One was a survey committee composed of physicians, and the other was a finance committee. A Westville industrialist, asked to serve on the finance committee, refused the appointment. He later encouraged citizens of Westville to believe that the "west side" of Midstate County had been excluded from the initial decisions. The editor of the Larch Republican paper, the author of the editorial series, immediately withdrew from further participation.

The appointed finance committee organized a voluntary subscription plan in order to test the way in which such a method might contribute. With negligible gifts received, the Midstate project, still in its initial stage, found itself without either a sponsoring body or an approved method of raising funds for the hospital.

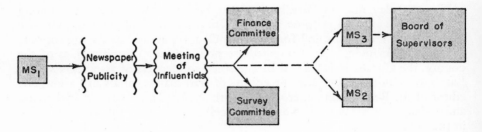

FIGURE 7. Midstate County Pattern of Initial Negotiations

Raising Funds

WITH the default of the "Sunday morning breakfast" plan the survey committee, consisting of physicians, prevailed upon the circuit judge to call a public hearing. Held in the Court House at Larch, the public hearing completed a petition to show cause for a bond issue. The election of approval, which was immediately forthcoming, demonstrated an overwhelming two-thirds majority in favor of the bond issue for hospital construction. To the surprise of many, however, the issuance of bonds was delayed. The unknown explanation was a disagreement between the appropriations committee (the county council) of the Board of Commissioners and the total Board itself. The chairman of the county council, a Larch dentist, was noted for his knowledge of county finance and had a reputation as "the watchdog of the county treasury." The county council believed that the physicians, by means of the petition to show cause for a bond issue, had moved to advance the hospital project almost inadvertently through the circuit judge to become the responsibility of the Board of Commissioners. The delay invoked by the chairman of the county council resulted from his legal and financial acuteness. Through a political contact in the Court House, the county attorney, the chairman learned that the public petition did not specifically state that it was mandatory on the Board of Commissioners to issue bonds. Thus, by rights of the office of appropriations chairman, he was able to forestall continued action on the bond issue. The survey committee, expanded after the public hearing into a formal hospital committee, did not attack the delay because of the turnover of personnel within the committee and the mounting resistance of the "west side," centered in Westville. In addition, the Larch editor, who had introduced the project on his editorial page, began to raise questions publicly about the delay.

The chairman of the appropriations committee, or the county council, was eventually confronted with another petition which, in effect, demanded that bonds be issued and sold to the extent of $200,000. This petition resulted as an activity of a new hospital committee. Formed with the aid of the circuit judge, this new group reportedly had replaced the physicians but brought in men who were "friendly to the physicians." Numerous references were made to the frequent meetings of the hospital committee with the County Medical Society. The second petition resulted in a form of strategy devised by the appropriations chairman, which provides a lucid example of what is meant by strategy and tactics in the present report.

The appropriations chairman was aware, of course, of a major center of opposition to the hospital project, namely, the town of Westville. This opposition was led by a Westville mortician and supported by the weekly newspaper editor in Westville. The strategy of delay devised by the chairman of the appropriations committee was that of the "remonstrance," or a petition which, upon gaining more signatures than the original petition to show cause for a bond issue election, would halt the issuance and sale of bonds pending an investigation of legality. It was possible to devise the tactic of the remonstrance because of the faulty wording of the original petition, which did not specifically make mandatory the issuance of bonds by the Board of Commissioners. The tactics of the remonstrance were in line with the resistances of Westville. The appropriations chairman negotiated with the mortician of Westville in devising the remonstrance, and arranged for a Westville attorney to circulate the petition in Westville and its environs.

The strategy was successful. The remonstrance petition was substantiated by the appropriate tax authorities, causing further delay. In the meantime, the size of the hospital committee was enlarged and its composition changed. Again, three of the seven members were Larch physicians. In the midst of the delay following the filing of the remonstrance, the passage of federal legislation and the assignment of construction priorities provided Midstate County with an advantageous position for securing federal construction aid. This event stimulated the new hospital committee to find some way to remove the delaying action of the remonstrance.

Members of the hospital committee, together with other supporters of the hospital, proceeded to engage in person-to-person contact, appearing at many county and community meetings. This activity was aimed at starting a flood of resolutions and petitions from local organizations to the Board of County Commissioners. The result was a hearing called by the Board of Commissioners to decide the legality of the remonstrance. Presiding over the hearing was a circuit judge from another district. At the close of the hearing the remonstrance was declared unverified. In this way, the delaying actions in the Midstate project were removed.

It should be pointed out that the hospital committee could have nullified the remonstrance simply by executing another petition to request bond issuance, but with legally correct wording and with more signatures than the remonstrance. Instead, the hospital committee contested the remonstrance. This may be explained by the uncertain history of the hospital committee as a centrally important agency of sponsorship, by public criticism received in the past for ineffectiveness, and by the rapid turnover of committee members. Facing the remonstrance was one way to demonstrate publicly, so local reports have it, that the committee had arrived at operational maturity. In effect, it was a "face-saving" device.

Organizing the Sponsoring Group

THE MOST inadvertent process in Midstate County was that of sponsorship. The initiating decision dealt neither with the feasibility of the hospital project nor the exigencies of sponsorship. Indeed, the project was initiated outside the domains either of associations or civil governing bodies. Not only did this bring about a series of unintended consequences; it made possible competing centers of decision-making with an almost aimless passage of sponsorship from one to the other. Frequently, divisiveness occurred within the group which held sponsorship at any given time. Thus, the appropriations committee of the Board of Commissioners was aligned against the parent Board on the premise that the county had espoused the vested interest of the physicians. Similarly, changes within the hospital committee resulted in an indefinite oprating group, serving finally to bring the organized medical profession back into direct participation.

The end-point of the inadvertent formation of sponsorship was a bi-lateral and competing arrangement. On the one hand, the Medical Society supported the hospital committee, which was appointed by the Board of Commissioners. On the other hand, the appropriations committee, although opposed to the hospital project, was a part of the major agency of authority, the Board of Commissioners. Meanwhile, the continued resistance of Westville provided a ready weapon for the strategies of opposition. That such circumstances could occur is explained by the failure to settle the burdens of sponsorship at the outset. Hence, the participants never knew, at any particular point, just what constituted the locus of sponsorship.

THE OVER-VIEW

IN Midstate County the towns of Larch and Westville are centers of all important activity in the normal course of events. What seems to be minor rivalries over competing athletic teams may become with the years struggles over politics and public matters. So it was when the idea of a new hospital unfolded on the editorial pages of the Larch weekly newspaper. Yet, the limits of the struggle are set in reality by the legal entity which includes both the towns, the County, with its Board of County Commissioners. Both Larch and Westville are autonomous units within the larger framework of living in Midstate County. Still, their authority is superseded by the actions that take place in the County Court House.

Getting things done in Midstate County is usually the task of the professionals and businessmen who live and work along Main Street of the two towns. The only agency of authority for projects of magnitude is the Board of County Commissioners. The articulation of the two is the problem of Midstate County. Building the hospital was a problem of getting Main Street and the Court House workers together. In many respects, this problem was never solved. An efficient solution depended on the successful formation of sponsorship, which became in actuality the most inadvertent process of all. The explanation for this was similar to that of many other communities and counties which suddenly have found themselves amidst strife, quarrels between municipalities, and delays within the historic walls of the County Court House, all because of a notion for improvement of hospital facilities.

For Southeast County the pivotal task of obtaining sponsorship was accomplished by acquiring the approval of the Court and the probate judge, and neutralizing the influence of the large landowners. For Midstate County, the first task was never clearly accomplished. This was the consequence of a disagreement on the method of raising funds. The disagreement actually was a manifestation of the old, old rivalries of Larch and Westville. A voluntary subscription plan introduced by a citizen of Larch simply meant to Westville that the proposed hospital was just another attempt by Larch "to get the jump on Westville." This divisiveness carried throughout the hospital project and made possible the strategies of delay within and without the County Board of Commissioners. Had the structure of initial sponsorship been clearcut, perhaps the divisiveness of Midstate County could have been as effectively neutralized as the influence of the landowners in Southeast County.

Still, the hospital-getting process did move into the county governing body. When this happened in Southeast County, the probate judge was picked up as an ally and included with the initiating decision-makers. In Midstate County, however, no member of the Board of Commissioners was added to the "inner circle" of decision-making, which was attempting to activate the hospital plan. Instead, the progress of the hospital was checked by delays of the Board of Commissioners, and did not recommence until a variety of events occurred. That the Southeast County occurrence did not take place in Midstate County was due partially to the difference in organization of the respective county governing bodies. For Southeast County the hierarchy of the Court was topped by the office of the probate judge, who represented not a prescribed area but the entire jurisdiction of the county.

In Midstate County, the Board of Commissioners had no manifest hierarchy, each supervisor representing only a specific township of the county. Hence, no office was so defined as to make it possible for one or more members of the Board to enter the arena of decision-making actively. Instead, latent arrangements within the Board, not fully known to the initiators of the project, resulted in competing centers of decision-making. The total Board had approved the project by calling the public hearing and by appointing a hospital committee. The appropriations committee, however, opposed the action of the total Board. This meant that the flow of the action toward a new hospital was blocked within the Board and did not emerge. No longer was the decision-making for the hospital held by the initiators; indeed, the next step depended on the delicate balances within the Board of Commissioners. The opportunities for delaying the project, rather than promoting it, were provided by the earlier disagreements of the two towns, Larch and Westville. Too, the mobility of personnel on the only visible approximation of sponsorship, the hospital committee, played into the hands of competing centers within the Board of Commissioners.

County-wide projects in Midstate County are worked out amidst a form of social organization not freely known to the participants. The pivots of crucial importance are two municipalities which are autonomous for most purposes and the Board of Commissioners which is traditionally defined with authority. Hence, if the techniques of ascribing sponsorship are overlooked, each town may attempt to capture the other. This was the circumstance in the turbulent years of hospital endeavor following the war. The circumstance is really the dissolution of "the County" as the actual framework for problem-solving, and in its place the emergence of the autonomous community. The concern for new improvements is becoming the preoccupation of the people who practice their arts and trades along Main Street, rather than that of the out-county political official, meeting weekly or monthly with his colleagues at the Court House. Yet, the emergence of the autonomous community in Midstate County is not far enough advanced to bypass the happenings in the Court House. Until it is, or the structure of county government adapts, the processes of securing sponsorship will continue to become entangled with the forces which still reside in the Board of Commissioners, and with those which change and solidify in the clubs and societies of Larch and Westville.

VII. FARWEST

THE MOUNTAINOUS terrain of Farwest County had impeded the use of hospital facilities in cities adjacent to the county since 1900. Hazardous driving conditions on mountain roads had brought about the establishment of a private facility of 12 beds in Marino, the county seat. When this facility was condemned just after World War II as a fire hazard, Farwest County was left without any hospital facilities at all.

Progress toward the new hospital in Farwest County began in February, 1946. A public meeting to discuss the improvement of medical facilities was held in the village of Crossroads, with a population of 800. The meeting was called by the local representative on the County Board of Supervisors. His intent was to combine an old interest of Crossroads, a new community building, with the new concern for better medical care. The proposal submitted at the meeting was that of combining the community hall and a physician's office. The latter was to include a few hospital beds for emergency purposes. The supervisor and the people of Crossroads believed that this step would help them to attract a practicing physician. The meeting at Crossroads yielded a resolution to negotiate with an architect's firm to draw plans for a possible structure to be built at an estimated cost of $10,000. Immediately following the meeting, public donations provided the sum of $2,500 to accomplish this purpose.

When the supervisor and the sponsoring committee at Crossroads learned, after a few weeks, of state regulations as to medical facilities, they began to doubt the wisdom of continuing the project as a single small community. A state senator residing in Farwest County was asked to discuss regulatory measures on the state level. At the second meeting at Crossroads, the senator discussed a California legislative provision earlier initiated by the Farm Bureau for permitting local areas to form legally-constituted hospital districts for constructing, equipping, and maintaining hospitals.

The senator from Farwest County was well known for a long tenure in the state legislature, his acquaintance with state officials, and his continuing interest in social legislation. He was considered a "friend" of Farwest County, perhaps its most prominent contemporary representative, and, for years, the able publisher and editor of a local newspaper.

The Crossroads sponsoring committee felt it advisable to introduce the notion of a county hospital district to other groups. Meanwhile, the senator described California hospital legislation in his newspaper, and the civic clubs in the two major municipalities, Champ and Marino, not only gave their support but became active in circulating petitions to request the Board of

Supervisors to call an election on the hospital district issue. The circulation of petitions was under the leadership of local physicians. As a result, a petition with 1,200 signatures, about three times the required number, was submitted to the Board of Supervisors.

Throughout the summer of 1946 hearings were conducted throughout the proposed district, and meetings of the Lions Club in Champ were centered about the issue, with outside hospital consultants present. In August, 1946, a county election was held. The Hospital District issue passed by a vote of 1,675 to 110, and a five-man Board of Directors was appointed by the Board of Supervisors. The chairman of the Board of Directors was a local construction engineer. Another member, later to become the most active decision-maker, was the legal consultant for the lumber industry in the county. Two of the remaining three members of the Board were self-employed businessmen, and the third was the operator of a local garage and automobile dealership.

After the first meeting of the Hospital Board in October, 1946, an analysis of the Board minutes, newspaper stories, and interviews in Farwest County all indicate that frequent deliberations of a small group of persons were characteristic of the activity of the Farwest Hospital District. These deliberations represented a closer relationship and seemingly effective communication between the various structural segments of the project. These activating agencies included the State Hospital Survey and Construction office, with the senator and the lumber legal consultant member of the Hospital District Board performing "go-between" duties; local meetings of the local Board, which occurred more than once each month; the County Board of Supervisors, represented in most instances by the county attorney; and the Medical Society, with the president as its representative. Meeting after meeting occurred throughout 1946, dealing with investigations of other recently-constructed hospitals, surveys of local needs, consideration of hospital architects, and determination of the required size of the hospital for Farwest County. These tasks continued until December, 1947, at which time the earlier estimated hospital cost of $900,000 (a 75-bed hospital) was reduced to $750,000.

In early 1948, meetings continued of the Hospital District Board with frequent invitations to participate extended to the Board of Supervisors, state hospital officials, local Medical Society delegates, and the representatives of hospital architect firms. The purpose was to determine the manner of acquiring required local funds in order to initiate hospital construction, in consideration of the forthcoming contributions from state and federal sources under the hospital construction program. During May, 1948, notice was given of a county election to pass on the issuance of bonds to the extent of $350,000. A series of six community meetings were conducted by the Hospital Board to acquaint the voters with the issue. In the June election the issue passed with a majority of seven to one. For the remainder of 1948 and 1949, meetings of representatives of the relevant organizations cited above resulted in construction bids being issued and accepted, construction commenced, and a hospital administrator employed. A close scrutiny of Hospital Board minutes indicates that throughout this period equanimity prevailed.

If this brief treatment of the major events in the Farwest hospital project seems to exclude incidents of resistance and opposition, it is only because this particular project was surprisingly free of difficulties. Obtaining a hospital in Farwest County was an administrative exercise by decision-makers who possessed exceptional access to state legislative and administrative agencies, enjoyed a publicly-credited body of resources and proficiencies, and successfully communicated with the representatives of the few relevant authority and influence structures in the county.

Only one undercurrent of opposition occurred. After the initial meeting at Crossroads in 1946, and subsequent movement of the project in the direction of a county hospital district, a prominent osteopathic physician in Farwest County raised the issue of osteopaths practicing in the proposed hospital. Under his leadership, petitions were circulated to gain public approval for the practice of local osteopaths. These, it was reported, were never released or placed formally before the Hospital Board. The petitions were withdrawn after the informal assurance by the Hospital Board that the osteopaths would have their rights. The osteopath, a member of the Board of Supervisors, participated with other physicians in the deliberations of the Hospital Board. He attended the majority of the Board meetings. This participation undoubtedly kept the osteopath issue both reduced and controlled until it was officially resolved by the passage of state legislation permitting "all licensed physicians and surgeons, both medical doctors and osteopathic doctors," to practice in district hospitals. This legislative decision was summarized in the local newspaper in July, 1949, after which date the issue did not occur.

THE FARWEST SETTING

FARWEST County was one of the original 27 California counties organized in 1850. Most of Farwest County is on the western slopes of the Sierras, and varies in altitude from 1,200 to 2,600 feet. The county approximates 1,028 square miles in area. Farwest County is in the heart of California's oldest gold-mining region. Gold has been an important product for the greater part of county history, but has recently given way to other developments. Lumbering and a rock-processing industry are presently the leading sources of employment. Beef cattle production is still a prominent means of livelihood. In 1948, 1,000 of the 4,785 county residents gainfully employed were listed as engaged in farming and ranching.

The total population of Farwest County is approximately 11,500. The peak in population came in the period when gold-mining was the lucrative business. The one incorporated town in the county, Champ, has an estimated population of 1,250. The county seat of Farwest County is Marino, with an estimated population of 1,655. Other small villages in the county range downward from a population of 800.

Ethnic Contrast

SPANISH people once composed a large proportion of the county population. Today many of the place names are Spanish. The Chinese were once numer-

85

ous, but in later years almost completely disappeared. In the early days of the Gold Rush, a great influx of population occurred from the eastern and New England states. Some of the descendants of these people are now considered the "old" families of Farwest County. After 1860, Farwest County attracted many Italian immigrants. The Italian-Americans are presently the dominant ethnic group. Italian names are conspicuous in the daily life of the county, in its newspapers, and on the membership lists of associations and fraternal orders.

Farwest County exhibits a relatively undifferentiated social setting. Major components of the county which would ordinarily denote status differences would be the several small towns, the out-county rural areas of relatively large farms and ranches, and the several large industries with employed executives and other officials. Despite their presence, however, a sharply differentiated social class orientation is not apparent. Members of ethnic groups, although they may belong to special interest associations, are considered bona fide residents of the county with every opportunity to participate in local affairs. Many of the prominent businessmen of the area are Italians and they are active in the public affairs of Farwest County.

The one important status ranking is that of "old family." To be "old family" requires ancestors who were early migrants into the area. However, a precise definition of what constitutes "old family" as to dates of arrival seems to have great flexibility. The Italian family who followed the Gold Rush days is so classified. The later settlement of the Far West mountain areas, with subsequent inward and outward shifting of population, has not permitted the crystallization of sharply defined status positions and the delimitation of distinctive social classes. The small population and the low density of population provide for ease in communication between the several small towns and the large farmers and ranchers.

Political Organization

THE SPARSELY settled and isolated small-town communities of Farwest County are integrated through a prominent county governing body, the County Board of Supervisors. Farwest County people believe that no other countywide group can sponsor county projects effectively. Regarding countywide problems, one informant stated, "The supervisors would have to take action sooner or later." Another informant summarized the viewpoints of others when the statement was made, "In matters of this sort (the hospital), you have to get past the Board of Supervisors." The Board of Supervisors does not have an integral officer as important as the probate judge of Southeast County. The Board's organization permits strong leadership through the office of chairman. The present chairman of the Board of Supervisors has occupied the position for 26 years. He is referred to as "the power of the supervisors" and "when he says so, they jump." Nevertheless, the chairman of the Board of Supervisors lacks the definite scope of authority of the probate judge. The local explanation is that since he represents one of the districts of the county, he must always confront the judgment that "he is making use of the chairman's job to help his own district."

In addition to the legal authority centered in the Farwest County Board of Supervisors, the members possess a measure of accessibility into regional and state political and administrative agencies. To a somewhat greater extent than in the two previous cases, the county governing body in Farwest County is related to the administrative and political developments in other counties and in the entire state. One of the important avenues to state agencies is through a resident of the county who is currently state senator. This position provides a point of convergence for the local Board of Supervisors and the state-level political organization.

Present evidence indicates that the extension of power by the Board of Supervisors into the districts which each member represents is not developed politically. County politics is not a "game" in the sense it is in Southeast County. Instead, there is a flexible relationship of the citizenry-at-large to the important symbol of local government, the Board of Supervisors. The Board is viewed as an instrumentality to "get things done for the county," rather than an agency to be bent to the will of a particular political group. The imagery of Farwest County informants sees current political incumbents in terms of their individual resources and skills, not solely on the rights of the office of supervisor.

As in Southeast County, decision-making in terms of county-oriented projects builds on two distinct roles. One is the authority for county matters that is built into the office of supervisor though the notion of office is much less defined than in the case of the Southeast probate judge. Indeed, the Board of Supervisors in its totality makes a more meaningful expression of authority and a locus of greater legitimacy than do the distinct roles of the members.

The second role, that of influence, is posited in certain businessmen, executives, and professionals of the industrial developments in Farwest County. They live and work in the small towns, especially in Champ and Marino. The large farmers and ranchers of Farwest County relate to decision-making principally through the Board of Supervisors. The organized associational life of the small towns makes possible the control of the resources and proficiencies for decision-making by a relatively few number of individuals. The influentials of Farwest County, at least those associated with the hospital project, possessed extensive access into state administrative and business circles. The influence structure of Farwest County is organized about the towns, with their attending business, industrial, and professional services. This differs from Southeast County, where influentials were the large landowner-storekeepers of the out-county plantation areas.

The interlocking of authority and influence in Farwest County occurs by tangential county and community-oriented associations, and by the control of the resources and proficiencies of decision-making by a relatively small number of individuals. Contrary to the situation in Midstate County, there is a lack of autonomous sub-groups within the county. In both Southeast and Farwest Counties the uniformly rural nature of the population, with accompanying small towns, provides for no sub-grouping that may seriously compete with the over-all functions of the Board of Supervisors. Only one town, and that not the county seat, is incorporated, thus possessing a municipal governing body with constituted authority.

Associational Tangency

THE ASSOCIATIONAL life of Farwest County provides three major types of groups. One type is the town-centered civic organization, integrating the interests of businessmen, industrial leaders, and professionals. In Champ one finds a Lions Club and a Boosters Club which have not only an immediately local function for problem-solving, but which concern themselves with county projects. Informants held Champ to be a "progressive" town because of the attitudes of several officials of an important industry in the county, the rock processing plant. One finds in Marino, the county seat, a Progressive Club and a Post of the American Legion with a record of activity in community and county projects.

A second type of association is that of county-wide organizations, of which the most important is the Grange. The Masons would be next in importance. Although the membership of the Grange is predominantly rural and out-county, this is not exclusively the case. Incumbents on the Board of Supervisors generally hold membership in the Grange. In the Masonic Lodge and other fraternal groups, residents of the small towns, farmers, and ranchers join in membership. If the Grange and Masons do not play initiating roles in county projects, they do offer a mechanism whereby communication and support are secured.

A third type of association is that of the Farwest County Medical Society. The professional position of the physician is one of prestige. The organized medical professional group stands as a locus of influence in all matters pertaining to the health, safety, and welfare of the county. Physicians participate in the associations of town and country alike.

An over-all observation of the associational life of Farwest County is that it is limited to a few well-known organizations, in which rather widespread membership is maintained. This limitation makes for simplicity and insures the articulation of the associational structure into the deliberations, arbitrations, and decisions of authority as represented by the Board of Supervisors. This condition was precisely the situation in Southeast County, where the only important county-wide association of extensive membership was the Farm Bureau.

Both sizable towns in Farwest County, as well as the smaller villages and hamlets, serve as focal points of county activity—economic, social, and political—rather than as centers of organized sub-groups of the county. Informants in Farwest County did not indicate a history or tradition of rivalry between these or other villages, as was the case with Larch and Westville in Midstate County. One explanation is the relatively undeveloped nature of the towns, all characterized by insufficient population, services, economic base, and constituted administrative agencies to compete seriously as autonomous sub-groupings. The gain of Marino and Champ is dependent on the gain of the county, and both are absorbed within the affairs of the county. Articulation of authority and influence structures here does not have to confront the situation of Midstate County, in which two sub-groupings, autonomous for practical purposes, are administratively encompassed by the political jurisdictions of the county and its primary agency structure, the Board of County Commissioners. Because of this identity of interest, both Marino and Champ are the visible pivots of county affairs. They do not limit their interests to immediately local activities, and both exhibit little community autonomy.

DECISION AND APPROVAL

THE INITIATING decision in Farwest County was provoked by the active interest of the hamlet of Crossroads in obtaining minimum "health center" facilities and a recreation hall. Both were to be planned under one roof. Then a variety of factors converged. Among these factors were the presence of state medical standards which made the original Crossroads plan appear hopeless, the concurrent development of federal legislation to assist with the financing of small hospitals, the permissive legislation for hospital districts in California, and the access of one resident of Farwest County to the policy-making level bringing about these events, the state senator. The initiating decision solidified when the senator appeared at Crossroads and recommended support to the formation of a county hospital district.

Following the Crossroads meeting, the senator negotiated with the sponsoring committee at Crossroads in order to secure formal cooperation for the hospital district. He next appeared at meetings of the civic and service organizations of Champ and Marino, and consulted with the Farwest Grand Jury which, in turn, investigated the alternatives to building an entirely new hospital. The senator, also the publisher and editor of a Farwest newspaper, editorialized on the need for hospital facilities and the opportunities made available by forthcoming state and federal legislation. These negotiations

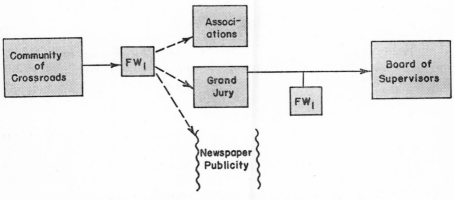

FIGURE 8. Farwest County Pattern of Initial Negotiations

were directed at two targets, the tangible goal of a new hospital and even more importantly, the formation of a specialized hospital district to deal with hospital affairs. The consequence of the negotiations was a completed petition, under the sponsorship of the medical society, which made it mandatory for the County Board of Supervisors to call an election for the hospital district issue.

Farwest County, in the initiating stage, compares closely with Midstate County, especially in that a newspaper publisher and editor was, in each instance, the initiator. Certain crucial differences may be noted. The editor of Farwest County also doubled as state senator and possessed the rights of this office, with its access into intra- and extra-community administrative agencies. The immediate concern of the senator was neither the hospital nor methods of finance, as was the case in Midstate County, but the instrumentality of sponsorship, the hospital district. In addition, the senator was confronted with hospital interest first localized in a restricted segment of Farwest County, which he immediately cast into the larger framework of the county. In accomplishing this, the burden for subsequent decision-making was placed on the Board of County Supervisors. The outcome of the initiating decision in Farwest County was to move the hospital idea into this centrally important agency of authority. The initiating decision in this case was solely concerned with laying the groundwork for a sponsoring structure that would serve to articulate the function of those holding authority and influence roles or public offices in Farwest County.

The decision of a method of financing the local share of construction costs was handled simply in Farwest County. This was due to the administrative permissibility of the hospital district. The Hospital District solved automatically the method of raising funds, for the District Board had the duly voted authority to levy such costs as the construction and maintenance of hospital facilities required. The problems of the Farwest County hospital project were solved at the outset by the negotiations during the initiation of the project and the supervision of the state senator. After these steps seemed successful, the physicians circulated a petition to encourage an election dealing with the Hospital District. The decision to issue bonds, after an election on the issue, followed after more than a year of planning with hospital architects. Visiting hospital architects appeared before the major associations of Farwest County. After construction costs were determined, the District Board gave notice of a county election to approve the issuance of bonds. By this time, the proposed costs of the hospital had been freely circulated throughout the county.

Organizing the Sponsoring Group

THE CONSEQUENCE of the negotiations by the state senator was to deal with the Grand Jury, then with the Board of Supervisors in order to gain a legitimate decision that a Hospital District be formed. Formation of the Hospital District would then result in a second authority agency, but it would be staffed by persons of influence in Farwest County. The district made it possible to organize authority and influence toward a common end. Conversely, it provided the possibility of competition between two competing authority structures in the decision-making process. However, no jockeying for the exercise of authority occurred. A form of co-sponsorship was developed. To forestall another complication, the osteopathic physician served on both the Board of Supervisors and the Hospital District Board of Directors. In addition to this, joint sessions of the two groups provided for continued communication.

In both Farwest County and Southeast County, the initiating decision-makers shifted the process to a county governing body in order to determine the appointments to a sponsoring or operating committee. The reasons differed. For Southeast County, the appointments provided the immobilization of influence that could be employed against the project. In Farwest County, the appointments to the sponsoring and operating committee mobilized proficiencies that were deemed essential.

Countering High Building Costs

FOR Farwest County the estimation of local shares of building costs was made after negotiations with hospital architects. The bid from the chosen construction firm was $900,000. The Hospital District board believed that the cost should not exceed $750,000. When federal funds became available to the extent of one-third of the total cost, the Board decided that the Farwest bond issue should not exceed $350,000. The course taken by the Board was that of arranging for certain architectural revisions and then calling for a new set of bids.

To discontinue the bids already received was no small problem to the Hospital District Board. The architectural plans and the bids had been approved by state and federal agencies, leaving the Board but two alternatives. The first—and the one elected—was the reformulation of plans. The second was that of acceding to the approvals rendered by state and federal agencies and increasing the extent of the Farwest County bond issue. A single member of the Hospital Board, the legal consultant, was dispatched to negotiate with state officials for a "null and void" on the plans and bids already received. He was successful in obtaining agreement to a reformulation of plans and a subsequent reduction in total cost of $150,000.

THE FARWEST OVER-VIEW

THE WINDING roads of the western slopes of the Sierras give the impression that Farwest County people live alone with their interests in ranching, lumbering, and rock processing. Farwest County has never been the kind of California which appears in motion picture, newspapers, and magazines. There is a physical isolation. Fast trips to the hospital over mountain roads in the middle of the night are testimony of only yesterday. Waiting for the doctor on the ranch in some Farwest valley is not yet forgotten. But the heart of the hospital story for Farwest County is that the people know little isolation from the affairs of California. For many of the people who made the Far-west hospital possible, keeping pace with the affairs of the legislature and the Board of Supervisors was no pastime. The story of Farwest County is a story of access.

Even the casual observer feels a certain simplicity in the organization of Farwest County. He notes that there is little differentiation between the people. There are, of course, men of wealth, and some of them had much to do with getting the new hospital. Yet there is little evident poverty. Whether one is a rancher, a businessman, or a professional makes little difference. All three center their lives in the two small towns of the county, Champ and Marino. All three belong together in the town-centered clubs and organizations which charter themselves for local government. Although Italians form the most evident ethnic group, they are not "across the tracks" people. Since the livelihood of the county depends on lumbering, ranching, and rock processing, the towns of Champ and Marino thrive on what happens in the out-county. In addition, the services of the two towns are so limited and specialized that autonomy for them is out of the question. Development of public projects in Farwest County rests on a base of communication between its people.

If there is any accorded differentiation of people in Farwest County, it concerns the estimations by county people of special skills possessed by some of the residents. A long history of gold-mining, and more recently of lumbering, has created a deference to technology and to its skilled exponents. Concurrent with settling the formation of sponsorship for the new hospital was the overt solicitation of men who knew about architects, bonds, and legal affairs. As people believe in Farwest County, there would be no logic in planning a hospital with the exclusion of men of engineering and law found resident with them. Too, Farwest County people admire matters that are tended with dispatch. Men of proven organizational ability were expected to enter the hospital planning duties.

After a study of Midstate County, one might wonder, in a first glance at the hospital account of Farwest County, why one agency of authority, the county Board of Supervisors, would be employed to create another, the Hospital District with respective legal powers. The answer to the puzzle is simply that, although something new was added, the old was not excluded. The Board of Supervisors was not only represented on the Hospital District Board of Directors, but meetings and planning actually involved both. The unforgettable strength of Farwest's methodical hospital campaign was the year-long concern with building the structure of sponsorship. Once this was completed, the rest was only an administrative exercise. This was undoubtedly facilitated by the opportunity to form the specialized Hospital District. Still, one cannot overlook what men of influence, resources, and proficiencies did to organize the capacities of authority and influence that rested within the county.

The organization of authority and influence into the structure of sponsorship was made possible by the state senator from Farwest County. He possessed the resource of access both to county agencies and to the legislative halls of California. As a prominent resident of the county who was making good in state and regional affairs, he was credited by the public with interest in social legislation, subject-matter competence, and a dedication to the progress of Farwest County. In addition, he enjoyed the position of being astride the communication channels of the county as newspaper publisher and editor. All of this resulted in his invitation to the original meeting at Crossroads, and enabled him to move the process from Crossroads to the county and the Board of Supervisors. In addition, his resources and proficiencies aided the senator in placing other men of proficiency in the midst of the hospital-getting process.

The completion of the decision-making process in Farwest County became the task of a legal consultant with a respected knowledge of events throughout the entire West. Although the senator transferred his responsibilities to the legal consultant, the progress of the hospital project still depended on a man of influence who knew his way around in the state capitol. As in Southeast County and Midstate County, once the process entered the county governing body it remained a county project. In later stages, the process had moved through the Board of Supervisors into the hands of the influentials, but the Board was never far away. Access remained the keynote of success in the hospital story of Farwest County.

VIII. NORWEST

In late 1945, a wealthy rancher and business leader of Norwestville, the county seat of Norwest County, with an executive of the county's oil industry, visited an oil field worker in the Norwestville hospital. This was then the only hospital in all of Norwest County, a small, privately-operated facility of 11 beds. Dismayed by the quality of care being given the patient, the two men arranged for his transfer to another hospital some 40 miles distant, located in a larger city of an adjoining state. After this incident, the two men agreed that something should be done about the hospital problem. First of all, they planned to investigate ways and means by which the problem could be solved. Local discussion was introduced by the two, concentrating on the personal attention by the Norwestville rancher and business leader to informal contacts with persons in Norwestville.

Informal discussions were conducted with the president of the Norwestville Lions Club, a county commissioner who might be expected to "question the idea of a new hospital," the chairman of the Norwest County Republican Committee, considered locally as a "good organizer," and miscellaneous others along Main Street of Norwestville. The explanation for the informal discussions, as given by the two initiating persons, was to discover the degree of support for the construction of a new hospital.

In early December of 1945, the rancher-businessman, who was also mayor of Norwestville, formally introduced a discussion of a new hospital to a Lions Club meeting. The members of the Lions Club unanimously approved continued action toward hospital construction in Norwestville. To give the project further consideration, a committee of the Lions Club was formed. The first act of the committee was to call a county-wide mass meeting to make the project county-wide, and to ascertain and record the reactions of the citizenry-at-large.

Following this county meeting, also conducted in Norwestville, a petition favoring a new hospital was completed. The petition grew from the meeting and the activity of the Lions Club committee. State law prescribed that if the citizens of a county collected at least $15,000 in subscriptions, it would be mandatory on the county governing body to bring to vote the issue of whether bonds might be sold for building a county hospital. A petition, therefore, was not a legally necessary procedure, but to the members of the Lions Club committee it was a means of demonstrating to the Board of County Commissioners that the proposed construction of a new hospital was "truly a county project."

The presentation of the petition to the Board of Commissioners led to the appointment of a finance committee by the Board, consisting of 13 members suggested by the Lions Club committee. The club itself was listed on the finance committee as a group member. The new committee absorbed the original Lions Club committee. As chairman, the Board named the local businessman who was also chairman of the county Republican Committee—the "good organizer." The finance committee's purposes were to expand the working group to include representatives of out-county ranching neighborhoods and subsidiary towns to Norwestville; and to devise a plan to raise the legal $15,000 minimum to show cause for conduct of a bond issue election.

Next there developed in Norwest County a county-wide organizational activity not encountered either in Southeast or Midstate counties. In addition to solicitation of individuals by members of the appointed finance committee, the women's clubs and other county groups arranged for fund-raising events—bake sales, dances, rummage sales, and "whiskey auctions." The result was that the original goal was over-subscribed to a final total of $19,000. This event led to the appointment of a Board of Trustees for the proposed hospital by the Board of County Commissioners. This group was appointed in February, 1946, about two months after the initiation of the project by the Norwestville Lions Club. It was the original Lions Club committee, especially the initiating rancher-businessman, who suggested the members of the Board of Trustees to the County Commissioners.

The events of the Norwest hospital project, from this point, relate to the activities of the new Trustees. The chairman of the Board of Hospital Trustees was the oil industry executive who assisted in the original decision to introduce the hospital building project to the Norwestville Lions Club. Informants contacted in Norwest County agreed that the five-man Board of Trustees aptly represented the interests of the entire county. This was a prime consideration in the selections suggested to the Board of County Commissioners. Four members of the Trustees were men; one was a woman. Three were business people from Norwestville; one was the oil executive, and the fifth member was a wealthy rancher's son who had recently returned to the county with a law degree. The latter choice was made to obtain the aid of legal skill in planning.

After selection and appointment of the Board of Trustees, routine events marked progress between February, 1946, and the spring of 1948. These had to do with selection of the hospital site, negotiations with architects, the development of architectural plans, and estimating the size of the bond issue. In July, 1946, the bond issue was approved by county-wide vote, received a highly favorable response, and permitted the sale of bonds to the extent of $130,000.

While the bonds were being sold and bids received for hospital construction, the costs of building had become greater than the finances on hand. Negotiations were re-opened with the architects, but it became increasingly evident that the original $19,000 would be needed for construction purposes. This sum had been solicited with the promise that it would be returned in the event of no construction. The Board of Trustees called a county mass meeting to gain approval for utilizing this publicly-subscribed amount in ways decided by the Trustees. It should be noted that approval was asked of the citizenry-at-large rather than an official group such as the County Commissioners.

The amount of the public subscription fund, together with the bond sale and certain reformulations with the architects, made it possible to begin hospital construction in early 1948. Although close contact was maintained with state officials of federal hospital construction agencies, the fact that the Norwest project had been initiated and construction begun as an entirely local enterprise made for difficulties in obtaining federal aid. With construction progressing and costs mounting, the Trustees initiated another bond issue of $25,000, which was approved by public vote in July, 1948.

In late 1948, the state agency for hospital construction credited Norwest County with a high priority for federal assistance. Local reports credited the chairman of the Trustees, the oil industry executive, with obtaining this favorable priority. Nevertheless, certain legal and financial technicalities demanded that Norwest County provide an additional $21,000 before federal assistance could be provided to the extent of one-third the total accumulated hospital finances. The additional funds had to be gained in a period of three days in order to meet prescribed deadlines. How this was accomplished is one of the revealing events in the account of the Norwest hospital project.

The chairman of the Hospital Trustees returned from the state capitol with a statement of the needed $21,000, and immediately presented the requirements for federal assistance to a meeting of the Norwestville Lions Club. The Lions Club members assumed the responsibility immediately, as a Club project, of raising the money. Someone suggested at the meeting that this occasion would not warrant "getting bogged down collecting nickels and dimes through passing the hat." The resulting plan was that the Lions Club would ask 21 persons to pledge $1,000 each, to be repaid when the state appropriated funds for hospital construction, a development then currently under way. According to local reports, this plan worked to perfection, as $17,000 worth of pledges were obtained without going off the main street of Norwestville." Federal assistance in the completion of the hospital was thus assured.

From this event until the dedication of the completed hospital in September, 1949, the activities of the project were routinely technical and limited to the supervision of the Trustees, with but one exception. The problem was that of deciding the manner in which the hospital was to be administered. There is a report of early resistance when negotiations developed with certain Catholic Orders to administer the hospital operation. The Board of Trustees formally presented the problem for consideration and discussion by Norwestville associations, especially the Masonic Lodge. The resulting definite decision was to arrange for a Catholic Order to provide administration for the hospital.

THE NORWEST SETTING

NORWEST County is in the midst of the Northern Great Plains. In 1949 the county had an estimated population of 4,200 persons and 1,300 families.

Eighty-two percent of the land was in farms. The dispersal of population in Norwest County is evidenced by a population density of slightly more than two persons per square mile. The population of the county is classified as entirely rural. In 1940, 33 percent of this was actually rural farm, while 67 percent was rural non-farm. The rural non-farm proportion is influenced by professional and business representatives in 12 small towns of the county. A considerable number of ranchers also reside in the villages but manage ranches in outlying areas.

The life of Norwest County is organized, for the most part, around its livestock economy. Seventy percent of the ranch income is from livestock. The businesses and services are found in the villages and hamlets. The county seat of Norwestville, with a population of approximately 1,900, is the major trading center for the county. The main street of Norwestville makes available the services that are necessary for the organization and pursuits of "ranching country." Five other industries are located in the county, however, which do not service the immediate needs of the area. Three of these deal with the oil industry, and two with specialized manufacturing.

Norwest County life is characterized by the livestock and ranching economy, and by the isolation of life on the Great Plains. The visitor is always confronted with miles of level to undulating dry land which intervene between the widely dispersed ranch houses.

Perhaps the major concern of Norwest County is with its "business." Whether one is a dispenser of services in Norwestville or Plainley—another prominent but smaller center—or the operator of an out-county ranch, the concern with individual and independent ownership is most evident. There is a fluid relationship between those who live on the land and those who live in the villages. The formal associational life of all Norwest County is concentrated in the 12 villages and hamlets, and the residents of the rural out-county areas utilize freely their economic, social, and religious facilities. Little, if any, differentiation is made between the representatives of the ranching industry and the proprietors in the villages. Hence, rural residents participate in the associational life of the 12 villages and hamlets, especially in Norwestville and Plainley.

Another characterization of Norwest County is found in its occupational structure. The major occupational categories are: rancher, businessman, rancher-businessman, professional man, ranch hired labor, skilled and semi-skilled labor (largely in the oil fields), and employed executives of the companies subsidiary to the oil industry. The representatives of all of these occupations center largely at Norwestville and Plainley for their associational life and the satisfaction of economic needs. Distance from the village centers takes its toll in intensity and frequency of participation. There is a decided lack of minority groups or specific ethnic populations. Great stability of Norwest people is evident. Negligible recent migration of population has taken place into and out of the county. Two-thirds of the ranch owners in the county had been on the present ranch for a period of ten years or longer. In addition, with but 1,300 families in the county, approximately three-fourths of these residing in 12 villages and hamlets, the organization of Norwest County is, if not simple, readily visible.

97

Although there is a low total population in Norwest County, and a low population density, an extensive associational life is present. In the out-county areas the clustering of a few ranches into a mutual-aid neighborhood leads to the organization of Farm Bureau groups and Home Economics Clubs as decentralized groups or chapters. Still, the real focus of associational life seems to be either on a county-wide basis or radiating from the village centers. So organized are the County Farm Bureau, the Norwest County Livestock Cooperative, and the County Grazing Association. Such county-wide organizations, in terms of official functions, center at the county seat. Village residents, often related to the ranching industry, share in membership in county organizations.

The villages, especially Norwestville, provide the location for a number of service and fraternal organizations. The Norwestville Lions Club was reported as the most prominent civic organization, followed closely by a newly organized Chamber of Commerce. In addition, the usual gamut of fraternal orders are to be found in Norwestville, such as the Odd Fellows, Masons, Shriners, various women's sororities, and the American Legion and Veterans of Foreign Wars. Although the list may not be inclusive, 100 associations were listed as having their official headquarters in Norwestville.

City-County Integration

OF THE four intensive case studies of hospital projects involving counties, Norwest County appeared to have the highest degree of organization centering around the county seat, Norwestville. This is the major trading center of the county, although periodic shopping tours take many local residents to larger centers outside the county and to one city forty miles away in another state. In Norwestville the Board of County Commissioners holds regular meetings, court is held, and the civil affairs of the county are reviewed. In the county seat one encounters the associations that deal with the technology of the county, livestock production, and marketing and grazing. The county seat is where one goes to dine with the Lions Club or the Chamber of Commerce, and where one meets both the business and professional men of Norwestville, and the ranchers and businessmen of the out-county.

The most widely read weekly paper of the county is published in Norwestville. To it the "reporters" of the isolated ranching neighborhoods send notices of births, marriages, and deaths, and news of meetings and social functions. If county-wide meetings are held, the odds are they will be held in Norwestville. Other meetings throughout the county are usually planned in committee sessions conducted earlier at the county seat. Supplying an important communication link are several officials of agricultural agencies who traverse the county but live in Norwestville. These circumstances indicate that to reckon with Norwest County is to reckon with its most important sub-grouping, the county seat of Norwestville.

As in some previous case studies, the entity of Norwest County is viewed as an appropriate agency for major problem-solving. This is explained, in part, by the small total population and its low density. Despite this, the county is not viewed by Norwest County residents as "the place where one is from," or as completely effective in the solution of local problems. Many of the problems of the livestock industry are met through the mutual assistance arrangements of the ranching neighborhoods. The highly specialized technological needs of the area are met through county and local organization of special interest groups.

Informants agreed that the concept of "community" is more than territory, characterizing it as where people "live and work together." Further, the informants held "community" to have two local referents. One is the series of out-county ranching neighborhoods organized around mutual aid and assistance, and the second is the trade area "extending out from Norwestville." Two in three of the informants included Norwestville as the "center" of the community, with "all of Norwest County" as the community.

Norwest County demonstrates certain focal points in the social organization within which decision-making processes are carried out. These are the governing body, the Board of County Commissioners, and the county-wide and village associations, which absorb jointly an influence structure in which the roles are predominantly played by businessmen, ranchers, and professional men who share in the associational arrangements centered in Norwestville. The executives of the oil industry possess varied proficiencies, as well as the resources of access and wealth, ingredients usually necessary to projects of considerable magnitude.

Political Organization

POLITICAL organization of Norwest County is similar to that of Farwest County. The important agency of authority in Norwest County is the Board of County Commissioners, with certain tangential offices such as the county clerk, county treasurer, and circuit clerk. No roles within the Board of County Commissioners have the prescribed duties of the probate judge in Southeast County. The chairman of the Board is considered the most active, and usually obtains this office through the estimations of status by the Commissioners. Thus, the Board of Commissioners is viewed as a unified agency charged with maintaining legal and civil affairs as they refer to the jurisdiction of the county, rather than as individual Commissioners with particular rights of authority in county administrative decisions.

In Norwest County the Board of County Commissioners is believed to be generally conservative, so that "if they go along with you, most people will know that it must be all right." To carry the Board of County Commissioners is to secure the cooperation of rural people.

From the evidence available it does not appear that the Norwest County Board of Commissioners provides access to state and regional levels. However, since the Commissioners represent the ranching interests and their service areas, they do provide an important link of communication throughout the isolated areas of the county.

As in Farwest County, the present evidence indicates that various localities of the county do not possess equally developed political organizations. Although locally organized clubs may encourage discussions of current political activities, politics is not the "game" of the county. Norwest County people are oriented to business and making money, and the issue of county politics moves alongside with little change and few periods of intense enthusiasm. The Norwest County Republican Committee works from the vantage point of Norwestville. This provides a framework for discussion and some political manipulation of local affairs, but the leadership is largely concerned with state and national political events.

For issues that must involve the legal or financial jurisdiction of the county, the Board of County Commissioners provides the major agency of authority. Although most county projects are not initiated by the Board, certainly true in the case of the hospital, local informants believed that the Commissioners would "have to go along" before the project could be a success. The initiators of county projects in Norwest County look to the Board as a group to give support by approving the project, but not for outright assistance. Local people have their own images of how individual members of the Board may react. Varying strategies differentiate members of the Board as to the way they may react to projects. The most usual reaction is explained locally as "conservatism."

In contrast to the preceding three cases, projects in Norwest County are initiated outside the Board of Commissioners and are frequently carried to completion without the active involvement of political officials. One explanation is the associational structure of Norwest County and of Norwestville, and the extent to which this structure is pyramided in certain centrally important associations. Every informant contacted in the Norwest case believed that the local Lions Club in Norwestville was the "best" organization to get major projects under way. Nineteen of 45 informants who responded to the question believed that there was no other organization in the county that could have initiated the hospital project. Others reported the possibility that some other group could have done so. Only one informant believed that the county Commissioners could have initiated the hospital project, and a few believed that the Farm Bureau might have been the agency of initiation.

When the Norwest hospital project was discussed and initiated, the Norwestville Lions Club was the one association tangent alike to the business, ranching, legislative, and industrial interests of the county. The officials of the Lions Club were also active in many other interests of the county, specifically the veterans organizations, churches, and fraternal lodges. The club included members to whom informants ascribed porficiencies such as "organizing ability," "legal knowledge," "knows a lot of people in the state capitol," and "good community workers." In addition, this civic organization contained certain informal sets of relationships between certain members which had been the "cores" of previous community projects. The initiating nucleus group for the hospital was included within the membership of the Lions Club.

The membership lists of each of the county-wide special interest groups—the Farm Bureau, Livestock Cooperative, and Grazing Association—include town dwellers, those who operate ranches and town businesses, and ranchers who reside in such towns as Norwestville and Plainley. In this way town and county associations are convergent, so that the Norwestville Lions Club includes a number of the ranching representatives and officials of the Farm Bureau. These kinds of linkages find their greatest depth in the Lions Club, which has the further advantage of being located both at the center of the organized life of the county and the point of greatest population concentration. The execution of decisions is facilitated with half of the county population immediately at hand.

Authority and Influence

NORWEST County, for such projects as hospital building, has both an authority agency and an influence agency, the former consisting of the Board of County Commissioners, and the latter the associational life centered in Norwestville, currently expressed in the Lions Club. Even the executives of the oil industry, who were reported to be infrequently active in local affairs, have as their entrance into county associations the county seat of Norwestville. The problem of Norwest is the interlocking of authority and influence agencies. In preceding cases, the locus of legitimacy for building a hospital was the constituted jurisdictions over legal and financial problems by respective county governing bodies. In Southeast County and Farwest County the governing bodies also participated in the initiation and execution phases of the decision-making process. This was true to a lesser extent in Midstate County.

Based on the evidence provided by Norwest County informants, and their images of "how things get done," the Board of Commissioners is usually concerned only with approving projects that involve legal and financial considerations, and not with initiation and execution. In addition, the pyramided associational structure, centered in the county seat with half of the county population immediately accessible, takes over a portion of the approving function. This is accomplished through associational concentrations of represented wealth, organizational proficiencies, extra-community access, and subject-matter (i.e., legal) skill.

This conclusion is buttressed by the hospital organization scheme in Norwest County, which went beyond a few persons representing authority and influence structures, to include more elaborate organizational machinery that evolved from and included the associations of the county. Thus, the community organizational process and the decision-making process in Norwest County operate with a more extensive responsibility on the part of non-political associations. This responsibility permits a portion of the approving functions, especially in initiation and organizational design, to be assumed by municipal-centered associations rather than by the county governing body.

REFERRING DECISIONS TO AUTHORITY

DEVELOPING a hospital in Norwest County, as in the previous cases, was immediately confronted with a necessity for formal initiation of the project. With a widespread feeling of need evidenced, the initiating decision was to have the hospital construed as a county project. This would involve the County Board of Commissioners, publicly viewed as "conservative" toward public projects. How this was done is explained by the strategy employed by the two initiators, the Norwestville businessman and the oil company executive.

The strategy envisioned was to gain the approval and public support of the Lions Club and then to move the sponsorship to a county-wide basis by shifting the center of decision-making from the Lions Club to the Board of County Commissioners. The first tactic, as reported by the Norwestville rancher-businessman then serving as mayor, was that of "operating on the street corners of Norwestville." The explanation for this tactic was that "we could get an idea of who would support a new hospital if we began to talk about it informally." It was also intended "to discover which members of the Board of County Commissioners would be likely to question the hospital idea." The informal discussions were entirely selective. The Norwestville mayor illustrated this by admitting that he was mindful of the fact that the president of the Lions Club had been in contact with a friend, a physician, who wanted to practice medicine in Norwestville ". . . . if the hospital facilities situation could be improved." The second tactic was the formal presentation of the hospital proposal to the Norwestville Lions Club. That these early discussions were successful is evidenced by the support which the earlier contacted persons gave to the hospital plan, and by the unanimous vote of approval from the Lions Club.

This process of approval did not halt with the Lions Club. The public mass meeting was sponsored by the Lions Club committee as a means of moving the project out of the Lions Club into the county's decision-making domain. To document the mass meeting, a petition was circulated thus enabling the approach to the Board of Commissioners. Not legally required, it was conceived in order to demonstrate that the hospital project was an "unqualified county project." This orientation secured, the Board of County Commissioners could be expected to enter into the decision-making process.

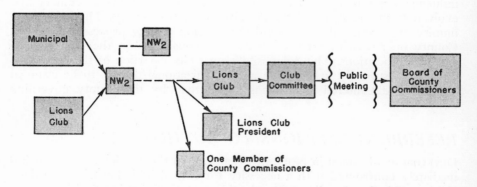

FIGURE 9. Norwest County Pattern of Initial Negotiations

Raising Funds

THE METHOD of financing hospital construction in Norwest County was envisioned as a bond issue from the outset. The desire of the initiators to move from the Lions Club to the Board of County Commissioners was, in effect, an admission that county-wide projects in Norwest County are usually financed by the bond issue. The device of the petition was employed in a different way than was the case in Southeast, Midstate, and Farwest Counties. For Norwest County the petition was but an extra-legal documentation of approval which provided a legitimate manner to approach the county governing body. The petition was not an open declaration for the bond issue, as state laws prescribed that if $15,000 was raised by citizens of a county for hospital construction, the Board of Commissioners would then be authorized to call for election on a bond issue.

The efficacy of the unrequired petition was that it enabled representatives of the Lions Club to negotiate directly with the Board of Commissioners. Negotiations on this basis resulted in a finance committee appointed by the Board of Commissioners, but suggested by the Lions Club. The finance committee added further guarantee that the project had moved from the Lions Club to an orientation based on the entire county. The finance committee proceeded to develop an extensive organizational machinery throughout the county, gaining an over-subscription of $19,000. The Board of Commissioners, with this evidence, appointed a Board of Hospital Trustees to investigate hospital construction and to recommend the amount of bonds to be issued. The recommendations made by the Trustees to the Board of Commissioners appeared as only an administrative exercise.

Organizing the Sponsoring Group

THE DISTINCTION of the project in Norwest County is that the locus of sponsorship moved through and beyond the major existing agency of authority, the Board of County Commissioners. This movement, unlike that in Southeast and Midstate counties, did not become permanently lodged with the county governing body. No authoritative office-holder was added to the organization of sponsorship in the course of passage through the Board of Commissioners. The eventual sponsoring group, the Hospital Trustees, proceeded to an alignment with the initiating decision-makers and the Norwestville Lions Club.

It will be remembered that in Southeast and Farwest Counties, the eventual sponsoring committees continued in either a subordinate or bi-lateral arrangement with the county governing body. For Norwest County the beginning and the end of the sponsoring arrangement were identical. Transferral of sponsorship was circuitous, but in the process added the sanctions of both the public and the centrally important legal agency of authority. Once the transferral was completed, the Board of Commissioners had but a perfunctory relationship. Indeed, subsequent decisions on finance and construction were directed to the Norwestville Lions Club to the almost total exclusion of the Board of County Commissioners.

Meeting Rising Costs

DIFFICULTY in managing excessive building costs occurred in Norwest, because the project was initiated before federal aid was made available. To meet the difficulty, three steps were taken. The first was to gain approval at a county mass meeting for using the original $19,000 (raised voluntarily to show cause for a bond issue) for actual construction. The second step was another bond issue for an additional $25,000 duly approved by public vote. By this time, still prior to the opportunity for federal assistance, construction was already under way. The third step, when federal funds became available and $21,000 was needed for matching purposes, was to obtain $1,000 pledges from the businessmen of Norwestville.

A distinctive note about the Norwest instance is that the same fund-raising method, the bond issue, was employed twice successively. In no other of the five projects did this occur. In Norwest County, when the final sum was needed, another method was elected.

THE NORWEST OVER-VIEW

THE PROBLEMS of Norwest County are simultaneously the problems of the county seat, Norwestville, in the midst of the sweeping swells of the Great Plains. Geographically, Norwestville is an island in the lonely lands of the cattle country. But in the decision-making process Norwestville is not an island nor is it insulated, as was Carlin in Southeast County, against the swirls and currents of introducing and completing county tasks of magnitude. In Norwest County the county seat is the pivot upon which planning turns. Norwestville is the place where the bulk of county population dwells, where clubs and lodges find their headquarters, and where rancher, businessman, and executive mingle on the corners of Main Street and dine together at the evening meetings of the army of clubs and organizations which dominate the life of the town.

The striking facts of Norwestville add themselves into two important elements. The first is found behind the store fronts of Main Street where men who like to make money do so but still find time to spend the evening at club meetings, to greet their friends, the ranchers from the hinterlands, and to pause on the street corner to debate the issues of Norwest County. The second important element is found at the end of the street—the Court House. Behind the sun-bleached walls convenes the Board of Commissioners. For all the importance of what happens on Main Street, the Board must always be included in decision of problems of a county-wide nature.

To maintain the balance of happenings along Main Street and with the Board of Commissioners, the burden of initiation falls upon the former. New events are born in the meetings, street corner discussions, and coffee shops of Norwestville. Rarely does the out-county area provide the focus for early initiations. On the Plains that begin at the city limits of Norwestville some people are found, but the observer will view, for the most part, land and cattle and oil. The people are in Norwestville. Some of them are from the ranches and most are from the dwellings of Norwestville. Thus, the population of Norwest County is pyramided in Norwestville. Then there is a second pyramid. Interlocking memberships of the 100 or more associations of Norwestville result in ascription to the Lions Club of the "top" position. If things get done, local people believe action will start with the Lions Club. But if things are completed, they will move up the street to the Court House for approval, and back down the street for the details of carrying them out.

In spite of such centralization, however, the affairs of Norwestville still concern the jurisdiction of the entire county. Although events may initiate on the streets of Norwestville, the people who walk the streets may live miles out on the prairie. While the club meetings and the business sessions of the agricultural associations may occur in Norwestville, they will concern the major industry of the county, the production of cattle. Since those who live on the ranches of Norwest County center their lives at the county seat, they, too, must enter into the arrangements that are planned along Main Street. The centrally important agency of authority, the Board of Commissioners, has as its jurisdiction the county. When a project is taken to the Court House, the county becomes immediately relevant.

The uniqueness of Norwest County's decision process is that most of what happens is free of formally-constituted authority. Even the pyramided life of community organizations, presided over by the Lions Club, does not provide the final word of authority as did the probate judge in Southeast County. Community action in Norwest County seems less predictable, but the way to obtain predictability is known to the leaders of the associations along Main Street. The pronouncements of officials of authority are replaced by the development of community organization for specific projects. Committees and more committees, public meetings, and a resulting sharing of the decision-making function occur within the already organized associational life of Norwestville and Norwest County. The hospital project produced, at one stage, a highly organized machinery to deal with the raising of preliminary funds. Few people and few clubs escaped participation. From this, the conclusion emerges that in the event of employing non-political and non-authoritative instrumentalities, a more complete mobilization of community resources is required. At least, such was the case in Norwest County.

Finally, it is Norwest County which demonstrates the growth of decision-making processes which thrive successfully on influence rather than constituted authority. As this comes about, the heavier burden of decision-making falls to the city or town, and upon the professional men, businessmen, and the executives who form and operate the clubs, orders, and lodges. These are the mobilizing groups for problem-solving. For the hospital in Norwest County, the major organizing principle was the associational life of Norwestville, specifically the Lions Club, rather than the Board of Commissioners. Until the Board of Commissioners finds itself with a superordinate office, one may expect the county seat associations of Norwestville to continue the initiation of county projects, to move them up the street for Board approval, but to bring them back again for completion.

ix. NOREAST

For MANY years the city of Noreast had looked with dissatisfaction upon the small hospital on a bluff above the business section. The hospital, an old converted dwelling, no longer met desirable standards. The happenings in the hospital on the bluff became the subject of joking along the streets and in the clubrooms of Noreast. As one person said, "The old hospital had become so crowded that I heard they were using the bathtubs for beds." Another stated, "The big worry of mine was that newborn babies had to be carried up two flights of drafty stairs from the delivery room." Gossip had been rampant when a local man was injured, was refused admittance to the Noreast hospital for lack of space, and later died in a neighboring hospital.

The Board of Directors of the existing hospital was aware of its problems. During meetings of the Board just after 1940, frequent discussions were held on the possibility of a new hospital. From 1940 to 1944, the president of the Hospital Board stated repeatedly that "his dream" was a new hospital in Noreast. The Board's tribute to him, on the event of his death in 1944, included a statement that his "dream should be realized."

Through this same period, the central figure on the Hospital Board was the owner of a local printing company, whose father had preceded him on the board. In 1940 the printer invited a wealthy landowner and financier, his lifetime friend, also to become a member of the Board. The two men began to work together in hospital matters. Upon the death of the Board chairman, the wealthy landowner became president, the printing company owner the vice-president. The administration of hospital affairs was charged with a new vitality. A new fire-escape system was installed, a new hospital supervisor was employed, and negotiations were opened with a regional hospital council. This was aimed at securing services which the council provided for small hospitals in the area.

In September, 1944, the vice-president of the Hospital Board read of the successful attempt of a nearby community to raise funds for a new hospital through the employment of a professional fund-raiser. With the Board president, he investigated the merits of the fund-raiser employed in the other community. Content with their findings, the two men discussed with the fund-raiser the possibilities of a similar venture in the city of Noreast. The professional fund-raiser agreed to spend two weeks in Noreast to ascertain its feasibility. This was done under a pact of secrecy between the three men, with the arrangement that the fund-raiser would report to the Board if the venture was deemed possible.

During the two weeks, the two officials of the Hospital Board contacted the local bank president to obtain a promise of cooperation in the event of a favorable report. The bank president abruptly refused his cooperation on the grounds that the proposed amount, $125,000, could never be raised in Noreast. As he stated, "This is a quarter and dollar community." The two Hospital Board officials persuaded him, however, when they indicated the extent to which they would support their interest by personal contributions. One other person then was informally presented with the plan. He was a wealthy vegetable broker, with the previous three a director of the local bank. He was reputed to "know the rural people better than anyone else in the county," and had long been prominent in the Noreast Lions Club. According to reports, this person approved the plan on the grounds that the bank president had accepted, and because of a history of cooperating with the three men in other community projects.

After the completion of his investigation, the professional fund-raiser appeared before the Hospital Board and presented a favorable analysis. According to the Board minutes, he made an "excellent impression." The Board members indicated that at the time of the meeting they felt some reluctance because of the possible "public attitude toward an expert coming into the community and taking money away." The two initiating officials of the Board observed that "the Board was worried about the expert and the bigness of the job. Yet, the fund-raiser had all the answers that night, said the cost would be less than 5 percent, which is as low as anyone could do the job, a local person or anyone else."

Informants indicated that the community-at-large supported the Hospital Board. The majority believed that the Board had the right to approve the action because it was representing the community, and that "no other group could have done it." But five of 42 informants believed that the Board should have communicated more with the community. Agreement prevailed that the professional fund-raiser was necessary because of the efficiency and competence which he would provide.

Following approval of the professional fund-raising plan by the Hospital Board, there followed a series of informal discussions, largely centered in the Noreast Club, a male social and athletic club. Presentations were also made at other Noreast associations, particularly the Rotary and Lions clubs, and an extensive newspaper publicity campaign was started. The professional fund-raiser soon arrived to organize the fund-raising campaign.

The campaign phase of the Noreast project brought to the community a complicated finance campaign. It was, in effect, a short-run bureaucracy. The four men cited above assumed key roles in a community organization that put some 600 persons to work. Each worker occupied a role with a title, answered for others below him, and to others above him. The goal was no longer the general idea of a new hospital, but had become defined specifically as a sum of money, or $125,000. The professional fund-raiser became, by contract and public announcement, the director of the campaign.

For the short period of the campaign, the fund-raiser brought to the community a new set of norms and a "short course" in the development of a bureaucracy. Workers in the campaign were trained in the tactics of gaining money pledges from friends. One of the basic rules was that of seeking out a relationship of friendship and of obligation. Each worker was given a maximum responsibility to select his subordinates, and to proceed to obtain a pledge from them. It was argued that this would encourage the subordinate, in turn, to be aggressive in getting pledges from his acquaintances. There was no longer a question of whether the hospital idea was legitimate, only of "how fast can the goal be reached." Note the following statement included in the written report submitted by the fund-raiser to the hospital board in securing the contract.

> From our knowledge of your community and its people, we believe that at this time we could recommend the well-known short term campaign in which the preparations are begun and the campaign runs its full course over the space of a comparatively few weeks. This short term campaign involves the rapid concentration of all the forces allied to the institution, and the application of this power over a very limited period. It can be used in your case because we believe sufficient power exists, because the appeal which you can make is now sufficiently clear in the minds of the public. . . .

> As important as is the development of man-power, it is also essential that the mechanics of the campaign be thoroughly organized; the endless detail of office routine; the proper development and checking of prospects to the best advantage for solicitation; the secretarial work of the committees, team members, and the thousand and one other things essential to a campaign.

For those individuals who played official roles in the campaign organization, speeches to committee and other group sessions were prepared and standardized by the professional fund-raiser. In addition, 64 different printed or mimeographed forms, letterheads, and publications were counted as a portion of the campaign materials. At least 30 different letters were prepared and sent to some 600 workers in the organization. A variety of operations was developed, including teas for the women, appointment of a great number of committees (Building, Finance, Rating, and Special Gifts), and planning and action meetings on the various levels of the campaign organization.

The intensive part of the campaign occurred in late 1944. By February, 1945, the original amount of funds ($125,000) was over-subscribed to $152,000. By this time the problem of some previous case studies became apparent, namely, that the amount on hand would not be sufficient at current building costs. The alternative plan of a bond issue was not considered. Instead, the available funds were converted into treasury bonds and the Board decided to withhold construction until a more advantageous period. No important events occurred until 1948, although during the intervening time encouragement was derived from the passage of Hill-Burton legislation.

In the fall of 1948, Noreast was given a high priority to receive a federal grant to assist in defraying hospital construction costs. The details of this event were handled through the office of the Gately (regional) Hospital Council, with the president and vice-president of the Noreast Hospital Board representing the local project in the negotiations. By this time the proposed hospital was defined as a 50-bed facility with an estimated cost of $480,000.

During the inactive period from early 1945 to 1948, additional pledges in the Noreast community increased the earlier subscribed amount to approximately $200,000. Since Hill-Burton funds were to provide only one-third of the costs, additional funds were required. These were obtained by a grant from a foundation, negotiated under the auspices of the Gately Hospital Council. The amount obtained was $92,000, which made it possible to initiate hospital construction.

At no time was consideration given to returning to the community for additional subscriptions or legal measures. In fact, as it was reported, the original four initiators of the project considered taking a personal responsibility for obtaining the needed deficit. With the details for construction handled largely through the arrangements of the Gately Council, ground was broken for the Noreast hospital in March, 1950.

THE NOREAST SETTING

REFERENCES to the other four cases were oriented to a county structure. Noreast is not a county, but a city with a population of 5,500 and a total trade area population of approximately 8,000. Noreast is the county seat of Mary County, and the community which it centers extends from the city in a radius of three to four miles. Ten miles to the west of Noreast is the city of Ripley, with a population of 7,000. Ripley possesses a functioning hospital. Ten miles to the east of Noreast is the city of Eastmont, which began to develop a hospital soon after the project was under way in Noreast. Eastmont has a population of 3,500. These are the three principal cities in Mary County, although there is a fourth sizable village, Mapleville, with a population of 2,000, in one corner. In addition to these population centers, a number of small hamlets are found in Mary County.

Noreast is located 30 miles to the west of Gately, a metropolitan center for the western part of the state. Gately is the location of extensive medical facilities. Some 60 miles to the west of Noreast is the metropolitan center of Oakton, which also sponsors major hospital and other medical facilities.

Mary County had a total population of 28,000 in 1940. For the entire county, agriculture is the leading form of employment, with some 3,300 of the total labor force of 11,000 so employed. An indication of the extent of urbanization is gained when the remainder of the labor force is studied: 780 persons are employed in a food-processing plant located in Noreast, 695 persons in services, 215 in local government offices, and 442 in construction occupations. The agriculture of the county is devoted somewhat exclusively to horticulture, the production of apples, cherries, vegetables, and to some extent, small grains.

Historically, Noreast developed as a stopping point on an overland transportation route. Soon afterward, stone quarries were developed, which brought an influx of Polish and Italian workers. With a later decrease in quarry production, these ethnic groups transferred their activities to food processing during their continuing residence in Noreast. Informants generally agreed that Noreast had developed economically from the basis of surrounding agricultural wealth, with the impetus of its county-seat functions.

Main Street and Hill Street

THE CORE of the community of Noreast is Main Street of the city. One hospital official in Gately stated: "If you want to understand Noreast you have to know what happens at the corner of Main and Hill Streets." From the four corners of Main and Hill Streets, where the city bank is located, extend the businesses and professional offices of the men who are organized into a series of city-centered associations. The city of Noreast includes the normal complement of business and professional firms, including two weekly newspapers, a prominent printing company, and a food-processing plant. An active labor union is present, related principally to the food-processing industry.

The "old pioneer" families in Noreast have been for years locally accorded the place of aristocracy. This is indicated by the Noreast histories in the local library and by the 1880 houses of Main and Hill Streets. In earlier days Hill Street, the location of "old-family" residences, was spoken of as "ruffled shirt hill." Members of three of the "old pioneer" families have been lawyers in Noreast through four generations. Another prestige group in Noreast is the business and professional group, whose businesses and offices concentrate about the bank at the corner of Main and Hill. Some of the businessmen are termed "near old-timers," meaning that a family residence in Noreast begins to count after a period of 75 years. The lack of long residence in Noreast was reported to be a difficulty in establishing oneself securely in the city. The transitory nature of the tenure of officials at the food-processing plant is noted as a deterrent to them in responding to social mobility motives. Many of the farmers around Noreast, moderately wealthy in the fruit and vegetable business, would be classified as businessmen. The label of being "old-family" among the rural population means less than it does in Noreast. City residents are not disposed to include rural families when fixing the caption of "old-family."

Another status category would be the working people, generally those who work at the food-processing plant, on the intensive horticultural developments in the rural areas adjacent to the city, and in the service occupations of the community. Among this group would fall the Italians and the Poles, who tend to live largely in a "little Italy" and a "little Poland." Both are located on the "other side of the Canal."

The Italians are moving upward in the Noreast social structure, and are increasingly active in civic enterprises and school functions. The Poles, conversely, participate in the community much less than the Italians. They still maintain their native language, and carry on crafts, parties, and festivals according to Polish custom. One informant reported that at the last senior high school play, the program contained not a single Polish or Italian name. Another informant reported that children who had been classmates of Polish children early in life would often require, as adults, a formal and new introduction if they were to meet at a public gathering. Another informant believed that the business and "old pioneer" families had been permitted to bring outside specialists into the old hospital for their care, whereas Italians and Poles had to employ the services of a local physician after getting a room or ward space in the hospital.

Finally, representatives of the business-professional group reported that the "old pioneer" family representatives had been losing in civic influence. The reason given was the precarious financial position which had come about with a decline in family annuities caused by the inflationary trend.

Problem-Solving Groups

As WAS the case in Norwest, the associational life of Noreast appeared to be an important dimension of the setting in which decision-making occurs. Significant here is the fact that the city of Noreast is a relatively autonomous associational complex. Although city-centered associations link with a few county-wide organizations, and while some rural representatives participate fully in Noreast, the total relation of city to county is nebulous. For Noreast, community problems are largely city problems.

Three associations largely composed of Noreast business and professional representatives stand out as particularly relevant to problem-solving activities. These three were ranked in order by Noreast informants as Rotary, Lions, and the Noreast Young Women's Service Club. Noreast people believe that the Rotary Club is the organization that could most successfully initiate major community and civic projects. Rotary differs from Lions in greater representation of businessmen and prosperous commercial farmers than that of the Lions Club. The Lions Club is more oriented toward the professions. The Rotary Club is viewed as a higher prestige group than the Lions Club. Significantly enough, not one informant spoke of a county-wide organization, such as the Farm Bureau or the Grange, that might initiate projects in the "community" of Noreast.

Located in one of the business buildings of Noreast is an exclusive male organization, the Noreast Club. Organized about twenty years ago as an athletic club, the Noreast Club now prevails as a dining and recreational center for its even 60 members. Owing to the selective recruitment of members, the Noreast Club is made up of those representatives of business and professional life who hold the keys to the influence structure of the community.

Since the Noreast Club is so expressive of the middle class business and professional group along Main and Hill Streets, it is viewed with some suspicion by the "people across the Canal." Some of the recreational pastimes of the Noreast Club are considered "too liberal" by the more orthodox groups in the community and, even among the members, some differences of opinion prevail as to the rules of conduct relating to drinking and card-playing. Since the objectives of the Noreast Club exclude the formal sponsorship of civic projects, it is not viewed by local informants as an important group for sponsoring projects. Nevertheless, one function of the Noreast Club is to bring the influentials of Noreast into a recurrent series of informal relationships.

Another important component of the organization of Noreast is its churches. The Italian and Polish population support strong Catholic Churches, and the business and professional people generally are active in the Protestant denominations. An important denomination is the Presbyterian Church, in which a number of civic leaders hold high offices. The religious orientation of Noreast enables the churches to be important in "putting things across in Noreast."

Noreast presents a specialized organizational arrangement not heretofore encountered perhaps because a hospital already existed in the community at the time the present hospital project was initiated. A Hospital Board was charged with administering the old hospital. Three members of this Board had assumed offices once held by their parents. To this extent, interest in local hospital facilities tends to have a family history.

Assisting the duties of the Hospital Board are the "Twigs." The "Twigs" are a series of 28 women's groups which maintain club projects that specifically render financial or material assistance to the hospital, as well as having regular programs of interest to the members. That they have a respectable tradition in Noreast is evidenced by their year of organization, 1914. The "Twigs" are composed of the wives of Noreast business and professional men. These groups encourage the transmission of hospital concern and duty from mother to daughter. In addition, the "Twigs" constitute one visible expression of the informal social arrangements of the women in Noreast. Although the manifest function of the specialized hospital structure is devoted to the maintenance of a hospital in the community, the latent function is that of bringing into an informal focus many of the associational and religious aspects of the city of Noreast.

Teams on Main Street

As THE "factions" of Southeast County were known to the residents, the people of Noreast are aware of certain "teams" of persons with a long history of informal and friendship relationships, and with a record of participating together in civic projects. People believe that certain persons in Noreast "go together," and that one can always predict this relationship in community affairs. These "teams" have developed from particular histories of reciprocal obligations.

Noreast consists of two segments, the city proper with its business and professional organization, and the immediate hinterland of a rural trading area. As opposed to Southeast, the locus of decision-making here is not in an out-county social organization but on the Main Street of the city. The rural hinterland is relevant only to the extent that a few commercial farmers have ready and fluid access into the associational and religious life of Noreast. In Noreast, differing community issues call forth differing segments of the community. Life is specialized in Noreast, and the way that the resources of the community are brought to bear on a particular problem depends on the manner in which associations view the problem as a part of their responsibility.

Although Noreast serves as the county seat of Mary County, there is no evidence of county political organization having relevance to the civic affairs of the city. The operation of county government is similar in Mary County to that of the previous cases. However, municipal concerns of civic importance to Noreast are resolved through autonomous arrangements. Even the City Council of Noreast has a limited domain regarding public projects, especially in initiation. Here the projects tend to be limited to the improvement and maintenance of the city physical plant, transportation, and communication. Much of the civic activity in Noreast deals with plans and procedures to assist certain service programs, such as the Boy and Girl Scouts, Red Cross, volunteer health agencies, recreation for youth, church "benefits," and the extracurricular events of the schools. Such civic affairs have little to do with the city's governing body.

The Noreast instance must be viewed differently from the other cases. Noreast is an autonomous unit that is not clearly linked to larger arrangements. An exception is the specializations in extra-community affairs. Noreast's decision-making finds its locus in an influence structure, expressed through the associations of the city of Noreast. Articulation with an authority structure, i.e., formal political offices, is not necessarily required for the successful operation of decision-making processes.

The foregoing does not mean that decision-making involving financial civic projects is wholly self-contained in Noreast. The hospital project was related to the Gately Hospital Council, which is concerned with several counties, as well as with officials of the Hill-Burton program of federal assistance. Nevertheless, hospital acquisition in Noreast was carried out through the presently defined capacities of influence, and did not proceed through an intermediate process to obtain formal political legitimacy. While foregoing case studies show that county governing bodies were active in various states, this was not evident in Noreast. Moreover, the Noreast project did not employ political instrumentalities, such as bond issues, to provide for the local share of hospital construction costs but, rather, a voluntary public subscription of funds.

Concentration of Influence

AN EARLIER cited statement provides a cue for the present analysis. "If you want to understand Noreast, you have to know what happens at the corner of Main and Hill Streets," it was said. The question becomes "What does happen there?"

The main corner of Noreast appears no different physically from that of any similar city. On one corner is the local bank, a branch of a chain headquartered at Oakton. Its second floor contains the rooms of the Noreast Club. Each week finds the 60 members of the Noreast Club coming and going from the bank building and the clubrooms for purposes of dining, a game of billiards or cards, and frequent Saturday evening parties to which wives are invited. Each week will also find five men meeting in the directors' room of the bank, and then retiring upstairs to the Noreast Club for lunch. The five men are not only members of the Club; two of them were its organizers twenty years ago. The third is the business manager, and the other two are popular members.

The Noreast Club was first begun as an athletic club, as an interest of two men. One was the son of a wealthy landowner and investor, newly graduated from a prominent Eastern university; and the other was the son of the owner of a well-known printing company in Noreast. The two sons had traveled together to Latin America on an extensive trip and had met regularly with others for recreational activities.

Today, the first has succeeded his father and is a wealthy gentleman-farmer and investor. He divides his time between Oakton, on business affairs, and Noreast, as a member of the bank directors and the only president of the Noreast Club. The second club founder has taken over the printing company. He is also a bank director and continues as a prominent member of the Noreast Club. The president of the bank, new to the community by some fifteen years of residence, serves as business manager for the Club. A fourth director, a wealthy vegetable produce broker, is the chief link between the bank and the credit arrangements of the rural people in Mary County.

This group is a crucial "behavioral set" in Noreast for the initiation and completion of larger civic enterprises. The public images of these men might be summed up as follows: For the printing company owner, "The personification of Noreast;" for the wealthy gentleman-farmer and financier, "Money and vitality, what else do you need?"; for the vegetable broker, "Knows everyone in Mary County;" and for the bank president, "No influence outside of Noreast, but a smooth operator when it comes to organizing."

The informal proceedings that take place daily in the Noreast Club overlook little that concerns the life and times of Noreast. Although the Noreast Club does not declare formally the sponsorship of particular civic enterprises, it does constitute an arena in which strategies are developed. As one hospital official stated in Gately, "When you go to Noreast to consult about the hospital, you will eventually finish at the Noreast Club and the business will continue from there."

Reciprocal obligations regarding civic activities are displayed and tested in the informality of the Noreast Club. For example, one of the almost legendary pastimes of the Club is the bargaining for civic contributions. It may be depicted by some such conversation as follows, flowing from a group of the Club members gathered informally for a "game."

First member: "I happen to have some tickets for the church supper next week. Each of you will have a hard time getting out of here without buying a couple."

Second member: "Your church supper is O.K., but the Boy Scouts are more in need of a donation right now. I'll pay double for your church ticket if each of you will throw in a little more to the Scouts."

Third member: "But the hospital needs a new microscope. I'll buy three tickets for the church supper in trade for five times their cost to the hospital."

And so on, step by step, until the civic good is accomplished.

In this way the Noreast Club, with some 60 members, not only represents the associational life of Noreast, but controls the official associational leadership. The associational structure is articulated and resolved by the events of the Noreast Club.

Three prominent associations in Noreast are said to be the "kind of groups that usually get things started." These are the Rotary, Lions, and Women's Service clubs. Three of the four men noted above are members and former officers of the Rotary Club. The fourth is a prominent member of the Lions Club.

The cases previously detailed excluded women from roles of authority or influence in projects of the magnitude of the hospital. The hospital-getting process in small communities appears to be essentially a male activity. For the most part, this is true of Noreast. While the associational involvement of women in Noreast is important in civic enterprise, it is still distinct from that involving men. There is even a counterpart of the Noreast Club for the women, the Silver Club, with clubrooms in the same bank building. From the Silver Club the ties lead to the Women's Service Club, the "Twigs," and the churches. Women make themselves felt in the civic affairs of Noreast, but they are subordinate to men in projects of financial magnitude.

The churches of Noreast participate as groups in the conduct of civic enterprises. They do not serve as the sponsoring agents. Foremost is the Presbyterian Church, in which two of the four men cited above hold active memberships. One is the presiding official in the church governing body. This official made a statement which indicates the manner in which the church may constitute a springboard into the issues of "community improvement."

> "If you are going to be active in the community, you have to have some group that you can depend on—that will back you every time. In my case, I feel that serving the community is one way of being a good Christian. Sometimes I'm not always sure that all the groups I belong to will back me up in a pinch, but I know the church will."

In addition to these core associations, there are a great number of fraternal lodges, professional societies, a Chamber of Commerce, (though reportedly a weak one), veterans organizations, and various women's clubs. These make up the club roster of Noreast.

The associational life of the Italian and Polish centers "on the other side of the Canal," consists of a number of ethnically-oriented clubs. The community activity of the Italians and Poles is focused largely in their Catholic parishes. A recent priest belonged to the Noreast Club, which provided some linkage. In the rural areas one finds the usual associations, such as the Farm Bureau, home extension clubs, and certain county-wide special interest groups devoted to the horticultural enterprises of the area. They tend, however, to follow their manifest functions and do not enter directly into the decision-making process in Noreast. In the hospital project, the county-wide organizations were depended on to assist with certain organizational and financial details of fund-raising, but they were not at the heart of the arrangements in Noreast that made, legitimized, and carried out the decisions which resulted in the new hospital.

SEEKING CONSENSUS

THE NOREAST hospital project began three years before its formal introduction to the community. Upon the death of the president of the Hospital Board, an active member of the Board, the printer, secured the appointment of a wealthy landowner and financier as the new president. The printer-member believed that a new era had arrived for hospital development in Noreast and he wanted a member of the community "team" in other civic affairs to be on the Hospital Board. In addition, the Gately Hospital Council was promoting hospital development in the Noreast area. Other communities in the vicinity had begun hospital construction.

The hospital project came to the surface when the two active members of the hospital board observed the successful fund-raising campaign in an adjacent city, and especially the skill of the professional fund-raiser who assisted. Both the printer and the financier believed that the skills of a professional fund-raiser were essential to their goal of a hospital. Before negotiating with the fund-raiser however, the two Noreast men proceeded to check evaluations of him by the community in question. Assured of the fund-raiser's reliability and qualifications, they arranged with him to "spend a few days in measuring the ability of Noreast to provide enough money." Only two other residents of Noreast were permitted to learn of the impending investigation of the city's financial base. Not even the other members of the hospital board were informed.

The first person approached was the president of Noreast's only bank, who had joined with the printer and the financier on previous civic enterprises. The response of the bank president implied that the suggested task was an impossible one—"too much for a quarter and dollar community." Yet he asked of the two men who confronted him, "What would each of you personally give to the building fund?" The responses were a surprise to the bank president, with the result that the bank president elected to join the two initiators with his support. A history of reciprocal obligations between the bank president and the next person contacted, the wealthy vegetable broker, erased any difficulty in adding a fourth man to those who already were in the midst of initiation. Both of the original initiators knew that the vegetable broker would follow the bank president, which enabled them to decide the order of the negotiations. Once again the "team" of Noreast had been formed.

The project was formally launched after the professional fund-raiser reported to the four initiators that his estimate of Noreast provided sufficient grounds to proceed with a finance campaign for a new hospital. He was invited to a meeting of the Hospital Board and made his report. Simultaneously, the two initiating members of the Board announced that the bank president and the vegetable broker "would go along with the project." The announcement meant to the other Board members that considerable personal wealth and organizational ability were pledged to the impending project. Before the Hospital Board meeting was over, the contract of the professional fund-raiser was signed. By this act the Board committed the community to a major project and simultaneously made legitimate the fund-raiser's entrance into the community.

The initiating decision for the Noreast project coincided with the choice of the fund-raising method. Since the Noreast project had no connection with either municipal or county governing bodies, fund-raising was never considered as anything but an appeal to the community for voluntary subscription of the required funds. That the method of fund-raising was the initial decision, and not the promotion of the hospital idea, may be credited to the combination of specialized authority resting with the hospital board with the mandate for administering the old hospital rendered by the community-at-large. The talk of hospital need was at a new height in the community. As the initiating persons reported, "the time was ripe to do something."

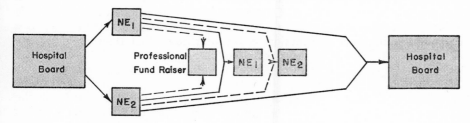

FIGURE 10. The Noreast Pattern of Initial Negotiations

Formation of Sponsorship

THE FINANCE campaign in Noreast, in addition to an extensive organization of the people, led to an impressive display of strategy and tactics. One example will suffice. As the campaign was nearing completion, the intended goal was reached. The professional fund-raiser then independently sent a telegram to the various officers of the campaign organization and called an emergency breakfast for the next morning. At the "breakfast" the campaign workers were told that Noreast was in danger of failing to reach the goal, and that another day of intensive activity should make for success. It is not surprising that an over-subscription occurred when the final tally was taken.

At first glance the organization of sponsorship for the Noreast hospital project appears simple. The Hospital Board for the existing hospital publicly served as the sponsoring agency. Yet, to understand the decision-making process, certain qualifications must be inserted. Since the Hospital Board was not an extension of a municipal or county governing body, as in Southeast County, the Board had only a narrow jurisdiction. In actuality the Noreast Hospital Board had a mandate to operate the present hospital, but not necessarily to build a new one. The decision-making function was largely carried on outside the Hospital Board. This is demonstrated by the character of the initiating decision. While the presiding officials of the Board, the two initiators, did recurrently confront the Board with their decisions, these deferences were designed to obtain successive "votes of confidence" rather than actually making legitimate the decisions already made. Much more important to the "team" of Noreast was the prevailing sentiment among the 60 influential men around the card tables of the Noreast Club.

The complex campaign organization in Noreast enabled the entire community to share the responsibilities of sponsorship. Once the goal was defined

117

as a sum of money, the organization of a multitude of work committees diffused the sponsoring obligation throughout the community. One might question the need for the campaign structure, since the initiating decisions had been effectively approved by the Hospital Board and accepted by the community-at-large. One reason is the advent of the professional fund-raiser, with a host of tactics in fund-raising which called for an unusual amount of interpersonal behavior. The bureaucratic structure of the campaign organization instituted, for a brief period, the impersonal order. When one became "chairman of the Special Gifts Committee" both title and office made possible a form of impersonal behavior probably not possible, or customary, in a decision-making process functioning by influence rather than by authority.

Bridging the Cost Gap

AFTER COMPLETION of the finance campaign, the Hospital Board for the Noreast project delayed construction until a more favorable period. In addition, the details of construction and design had not been considered prior to raising the funds. The community-at-large believed that the problem of design belonged to the Hospital Board, because "it had been looking hospitals over for several years." This public image of the competence for the "team" of Noreast permitted the alteration in sequence.

In Noreast $152,000 was raised through voluntary public subscription. The Hospital Board, with only an explanation that building costs would not permit immediate construction, converted the funds into treasury bonds. Still with no promise of federal assistance, active entry was made into the programs of the Gately Hospital Council. This entry strengthened the access which members of the Noreast Board already had with the Gately Council and set the stage for assistance from this source.

During the period of inactivity, 1945–1948, federal assistance became available. Detailed planning was then resumed. By this time, the estimated total cost was $480,000. The proposed federal grant was $100,000 and the Noreast contribution had swelled to $200,000 by 1948. The remaining amount, in no surprising fashion to townsmen, was negotiated by the printer, through the Gately Hospital Council, with a major health foundation. Again, the resource of access had come to the rescue. Between 1945 and 1948, the old Noreast hospital had become one of the more responsible members of the Gately Hospital Council. The interests of the Gately Council in the improvement of hospital administration had been advanced by the leaders in Noreast. In this way the Noreast hospital project, as did others, rested in a larger framework of activity and interest.

THE NOREAST OVER-VIEW

THE HOSPITAL projects in Farwest County, and to a greater extent in Norwest County, began to move to the main streets of concerned towns and cities. In Noreast, most of what happened occurred at the corner of Main and Hill. The interplay between the bank directors, the Noreast Club that meets over the bank, and the Rotary Club rooms diagonally across the corner—each and all made the hospital a reality. The Noreast project was not the work of governing bodies with county and municipal jurisdictions. Nor was Noreast the setting for bond issues, a public referendum, and legal red tape. Instead, Noreast was a small city that obtained a hospital because of four men's work with each other and with most of those who have the address of "Noreast."

Civic improvement is a continuing interest of the city of Noreast. Around this theme are organized many discussions of the exclusive clubs, and of those who make their living "across the counters" on Main Street. Moving upward in the estimation of Noreast is aided by promoting the countless benefit suppers, by helping the Boy Scouts, by giving aid to the poor at Christmas, and by making sure "that Noreast is better than any other town." In the way that these smaller matters are acted out lies the explanation for major civic problem-solving in Noreast. One cannot do it alone. Instead, he joins with old friends in the comfort of the Noreast Club, at the dining tables of the Rotary and Lions clubs, and at the myriad of meetings held in the hospital, the bank, and the back room of the town's foremost printer.

Civic improvement in Noreast is the task of community "teams." For important projects there is but one "team." As one initiator of the Noreast project, the printer, stated, "It was time for 'us' to do something." The "us" was not the community, but the printer, himself, and the three other members of the "team." The "team" was not built on any mandate, nor on a struggle of commitment. Instead, the "team" was a consequence of history. Three young men had started it all twenty-five years ago with a weekly game of poker. After managing a bachelor's trip abroad, the next pastime became an athletic club. The new bank president provided rooms over the bank and agreed to serve as the club manager.

Although the years have changed the purpose of the Noreast Club, its 60 members still maintain the original initiators as officers. Yet, the Noreast Club was not the only outcome of this association. Only the four men know exactly how each has helped the other—in the introduction of two of them to the active life of the community, or the time the bank president saved one by the negotiation of notes, and when one helped another in "putting the Presbyterian Church on its feet." So it is—in a mixture of friendship, nostalgia, and obligation—that the "team" of Noreast still meets at the corner of Main and Hill and still holds itself accountable for civic improvement.

Beyond this, the "team" of Noreast is more than four men. It really has the control of the town associations of greater and lesser influence. With the added possession of great personal resources and proficiencies, few can deny that what the "team" selects as a task is "bound to succeed rather than fail." There is no official mandate for its work but Noreast still feels—as it has for many years—that "these are the kind of men that every community needs."

In the other four cases, county governing bodies possessed general and constituted rights to be concerned with hospital decision-making. For Noreast there was no authority agency involved with general rights in decision-making for civic projects. Instead, a few influential persons were accorded tacit permission for general decision-making. The only agency with a vestige of authority, the Hospital Board, was specific in its function. As compared with Southeast County, Noreast was a reversal. The problem of getting a hospital in Noreast was the organization of influence, all without official mandate and without constituted authority.

But, as many people in Noreast implied, more than influence is required in getting dollars out of pockets into the hospital building fund. This is where the top influence agent of all entered the process. The professional fund-raiser, with proficiency as an asset, added the formula which the Noreast instance required. The formula was a compact package of organization, emotion, slogans, work, committees, and brevity. The professional fund-raiser's formula enabled friend to contact friend, kin to solicit kin, colleague to stimulate colleague. To solicit as a friend is one thing. To solicit as an official in the campaign is another. The formula provided that everyone should perform. In addition, the campaign evolved amidst a climate of impending crisis. Slogans, appeals, poetry, and admonishment all called forth the pride in one's own home town. The result of the formula was a new hospital in Noreast.

Now the hospital has been dedicated, another successful endeavor of the "team." No doubt the people say again, "Whatever 'they' begin they always finish." Some will wonder what may happen when the "team" will no longer be active. The evidence in the Noreast instance suggests that as long as the pyramided structure of associations continues, there will be someone to fill the vacancies and maintain the "team."

x. POSITION AND AUTHORITY

ACQUIRING a hospital, like other developments toward health facilities, takes place within specified social arrangements. Nevertheless, the decisions and actions of the men and women in small-town America are at the heart of the story. This makes worth-while an acquaintanceship with those who received the greatest credit for success in acquiring a hospital. Twenty men in the five hospital projects were accorded the greatest number of choices of their people for what they had contributed to the hospitals. Some stayed in the process from start to finish. Others did not. Few were old and few were young. Some were rich, but none were poor. What they had in common was the right to make decisions affecting the hospital. Some had authority and some had influence. Some had both.

Following is a series of 20 brief case studies. Each aims to portray the ingredients of the quality of authority possessed by a high-ranked participant. Thus, each case has to do with the positions held within the community, the possessions of family, kinship, and occupational status, and the offices which gave the incumbent special privilege when entering the decision-making process. Of supplementary importance will be the viewpoints of the community-at-large as to these positions and offices.

Southeast County

SE₁ The individual ranked highest for "what he did for the hospital" was male, middle-aged, and the owner of a large plantation on the edge of the Black Belt. He was the owner and operator of a prominent out-county store. Although a native of Southeast County, he had left in his youth and had risen to an executive position in a large business establishment in a northern state. After returning in the early days of World War II, he became active in community and county affairs. He reported, "My business job of the last several years kept me traveling over the country, and I never knew what it meant to work in one's home community. This is one reason why I wanted to come back to Southeast County."

The one organization in which SE₁'s desires were immediately realized was that of the Farm Bureau. He served as president through three critical years in the organization, 1944–1947. Southeast County people believed that he had been encouraged to accept Farm Bureau leadership because of "his business experience up north," and his facility "to ramrod things through, in spite of opposition." In 1947, the following resolution was unanimously passed by the directors of the Southeast County Farm Bureau.

Whereas Mr. (SE₁) who, for three years, served as president of the Southeast County Farm Bureau, taking charge when the membership totaled 53 members, and said membership grew to 887 under his leadership, did through his unselfish and wholehearted effort promote the Southeast County Farm Bureau to the largest membership in its history, now therefore, the officers and directors do hereby express our deep appreciation for his wonderful service.

The major access which SE_1 had to county-wide events was that of the Farm Bureau. The following selected quotations made by informants are indicative: "He was a very active member of the Farm Bureau"; "He came back at the low ebb of the Farm Bureau, and made a good president in building it back"; "He is popular with the Farm Bureau; goes out and gets new men for their vitality."

The singular nature of the Farm Bureau as the only county-wide association incorporating both the influential large landowner-store keepers and political officials indicates that the office of president gave its incumbent entrance into the organized life of the county.

SE_2 Ranked as the second most important in the decision-making role was the probate judge. This office had two incumbents during the hospital project. Informants agreed that the way to accomplish public purposes in Southeast County was through the political mechanism. Overwhelming testimony was given to the ascendency of the office of probate judge in all political and some non-political matters. Earlier references to the office of probate judge in Southeast County, supported by the observations of others, suffice to indicate that legal and financial concerns of the county became squarely the task of the probate judge for decision and administration.

The two incumbents of the office of probate judge during the period of the hospital project differed in that the prior judge was linked closely to the affairs of Carlin, the county seat of the Black Belt, while his successor, on the event of the former's death, was reported aligned with the "hill country." In regard to the probate judge at the time of the initiation of the hospital, the following sample statements are indicative of the authority constituted in the office.

"If Judge SE_2 had lived, and said 'do it,' the Court would have supported it."

"The Court would always back him on business affairs."

"He told people what they could do and that the county was not able to build a hospital, but if they would really want it he would appoint a board and let them work it out in any way they saw fit."

"As probate judge he was a powerful man in this county."

"One of the greatest citizens we've ever had, but if he had lived I don't believe we'd have the hospital."

After the original hospital committee was appointed, the initial probate judge died and a successor was appointed by the state who was not generally accepted in the Black Belt. In spite of a public imagery that focused on his "lack of family background and education," the constituted rights of the office enabled him to be active in the hospital project. Actually, with the shift in political administration of the county through state appointment of the probate judge, the Court Commissioners were opposed to continuing with the hospital project.

The new probate judge individually supported the project in the face of this opposition, as well as that coming from a political faction centered in his own area, the "hill country." The stand of the new probate judge was felt by many informants to be a political overture to the voters of low income portions of the county, "who were led to believe that the hospital would result in low cost, if not free, medical care." Regardless of the motivation, that the new judge could make this stand was inherent in the rights of his office as probate judge. The following sample statements made by informants are indicative.

"If he is for you, he is for you; if he's against you, heaven take you."

"Used his influence with the state. Only about one-third of the counties that applied got state funds."

Although the role of probate judge has both constituted rights and those defined by tradition in a situation culturally oriented to the solution of local problems by political instrumentalities, additional arrangements within the County Commissioner's Court place the incumbent in full communication with continually shifting factional alignments. For instance, much of the traditional Court activity dealt with the administration and maintenance of roads. Accordingly, each commissioner was given responsibility, and a small budget, for the maintenance of the roads in his district. The probate judge makes the allotments to the commissioners. Such devices, "built into" the Commissioner's Court, provide for transactions and negotiations affecting the entire population of the county. Note the following comment by a county official:

"[One County Commissioner] didn't put a road back into [a locality] and all the [a kinship system] banded together and beat him in every beat except his own. I don't think he will ever try to come back."

Several informants believed that the office of probate judge is not presently as well defined in the rights accruing to it as formerly. This is accredited to the lack, due to technological changes, of a neatly-articulated political out-county organization. Especially significant is the change in the political function of the plantation store from what it was in the cotton culture of the earlier Black Belt. The following statement is representative of many dealing with this observation.

"The problem of modern politics in [Southeast County] is that the best thinking people are now not only the ones concerned in politics, but the poor thinking people now have their own political leaders and must be reckoned with. At one time the people in politics were all 'old family,' going back for three generations, with prestige, money, and responsibility; while presently a lot of people interested in politics are always over-confident. This is dangerous in [Southeast County] politics."

SE_3 The individual ranked third highest by the informants in regard to "what he did for the hospital" was male, 42 years of age, educated in two prominent universities of the South, and a member of the family that owned the largest acreage of land in Southeast County. His family represented an old lineage in the Black Belt, having originally "come from South Carolina." SE_3 joins with a slightly older brother in managing extensive cattle and cotton enterprises. In most respects, SE_3 represented the influence vested in the large landowner-storekeepers of Southeast County. The family operates one of the traditional plantation stores.

SE_3 held three important offices and positions. First, there was active participation in the two important county-wide associations, the Farm Bureau and the Cattlemen's Association. He had served over a period of time as a director of both, and more recently had succeeded SE_1 as the president of the Farm Bureau. Second, store ownership must be considered an influential position in view of the large number of tenants and other workers employed in the extensive farming operations of the family. Third, there were extensive positional aspects of family and kinship.

Active participation in the Farm Bureau had led to SE_3's role as an "influencer" *within* the Farm Bureau, while SE_1 was more active as an "organizer" in representing the Farm Bureau in county affairs. The following comments from selected informants are indicative of the manner in which SE_3 was related to the Farm Bureau.

> "He's a good man, and has been active in the Farm Bureau ever since he was a boy."

> "When it comes to the Farm Bureau, he could have sabotaged the whole project in spite of the energy of [SE_1]."

> "He is a mighty good man and a worker, *as well as in the Farm Bureau*." (Italics ours)

> "Has a lot of influence with the young group and the Farm Bureau."

> "He always spoke for the hospital *in the Farm Bureau*." (Italics ours)

SE_4 The individual ranked fourth in making the hospital a reality was the manager of a distributing company in Carlin. General agreement prevailed that influence of SE_4, a relative newcomer to Carlin, was limited to the immediate affairs of the county seat rather than in the out-county Black Belt or hill country areas. SE_4 entered into project activities at a relatively late stage. The explanation was his membership on the Carlin town council and the subsequent importance of this council in the selection and securing of the hospital building site. The important positional element to be attributed to SE_4, therefore, was membership on the Carlin town council. In addition, he had an interest in state politics and a plan to contest for state representative. The municipal governing role provided access to the prominent—some of them "old family"—representatives of the educational and associational life of Carlin.

A second major office held by SE_4 was trusteeship of both Broadview

College and Carlin Military Academy. An earlier reference pointed out the importance of these two institutions for the people of Carlin. SE_4 had been active in fund-raising campaigns to "save" Broadview College, and this performance had enabled even a newcomer to successfully identify with those of position and influence in Carlin.

> "He is on the city command of Carlin, the Board of Trustees of Carlin Military Academy, and well thought of by a certain group of people in Carlin."

> "He is a city council man, and interested in the hospital from the city's point of view."

> "He was on the draft board during the War, and carries a lot of weight in Carlin."

Midstate County

MS_1 The decision-maker who initiated the idea for a new hospital in Midstate County was, in a positional sense, the editor of the weekly newspaper in the county seat of Larch. Thus, he controlled a major medium of communication. MS_1, a relative newcomer to Larch, brought to his position a particular body of experience and a self-image that was somewhat in conflict with the expectations of the various decision-making publics in Midstate County.

The experience of MS_1 was employment on metropolitan newspapers following college training in journalism. In addition, he had gained some "felt skills" in promotional work for community welfare activities, especially fund-raising. From this, MS_1 had developed a definition of the newspaper man as the "watchdog" of community developments. Although his series of articles actually informed the community of hospital need and introduced the possibility of a new hospital, his role later shifted to a careful perusal of the detail of hospital project events, followed by publication in the newspaper. Such behavior repeatedly ran counter to the expectations of other decision-makers. In addition, MS_1 was not averse to rebuking his own political party editorially. This alienated him from officials of the Republican Party in Midstate County. An example of his direct approach was reported thus:

> A local businessman had been involved in an accident in which a small boy had been injured. It had been rumored that he had, in turn, sent the boy and his mother away "to let the thing cool off." MS_1 insisted on printing the story with the resulting alienation of business people and a loss in advertising.

MS_2 Only in Midstate and Farwest Counties were physicians active as members of the "inner circle" of decision-making. In Midstate County, a physician was viewed as a centrally important participant in the hospital project. Positionally, his important office, in addition to physician, was that of president of the County Medical Society. Informants generally believed that once the project had been initiated, and had encountered difficulty, the sustaining interest in the hospital had come from the medical society, and specifically its leader, MS_2. Another influence was MS_2's active participation in the civic organizations of Larch. Several informants advanced some such comment as, "He is an outstanding man and the best doctor in town. He is very well liked and worked hard for the hospital." An early symbolic expression of need for a hospital by residents of Larch was that "the lack of a local hospital kept the physicians driving to other hospitals, which was not only hazardous but reduced local practice." This expression, made by many, usually referred to MS_2.

Added to the office of Medical Society president, MS_2 had formerly been a basketball coach in Westville. His success in this pre-medical career occupation had, as one said, "endeared him to Westville people." The following comments made by Larch informants should be noted.

"He is a man with real influence in Westville, and can talk to the better people there."

"If [MS_2] had lived in Westville, the hospital would have carried Westville."

MS_3 In Southeast County two of the four high-ranked decision-makers possessed an office of county or municipal governing responsibility. Reported central in the Midstate project was the political office of circuit judge, termed here MS_3. Born and reared in Midstate County, MS_3 enjoyed the positive image throughout the county of having been "a local boy who had made good." This image resulted from the assumption of individual responsibilities in completing law school under adverse conditions, and of following a former outstanding judge.

Although the office of circuit judge is political in a formal sense, it is not included within the structure of the county governing body. The "out-of-court" functions of this office were defined, both by the incumbent and other informants, to include the expediting of county affairs that require a source of legal knowledge. Such a contribution was accepted as non-political behavior, and no mention was made of the function being included in the rights and duties of the office. Throughout the development of the Midstate project, MS_3 accepted the responsibility of bringing legal knowledge to the sponsoring group for the hospital. At the point where the need no longer existed, the circuit judge withdrew from further participation.

MS_4 It should be noted that the Midstate project was characterized by professional men participating positively in the decision-making process. This was not true of Southeast County. The fourth individual to be included, and reported as the most active participant, was a Larch druggist. Although the public image would cast him more as "a successful businessman" than a professional man, his position was at a convergent point of interest, and a subsequently developed relationship, with the medical profession. Although he held no offices in the formal political sense or in the relevantly important associations in Larch, he did possess access to them. One informant believed that he "reported to the county commissioners more than was necessary."

Due to an uncertain public image, it is doubtful that MS_4 possessed the capacity of influence. However, intra- and extra-community access made him appear, both to the public and to other decision-makers, as "most active."

This explains his extensive operations in the role of, as one informant put it, "traveler" for the hospital development in petition circulation, consultation, and negotiation with the officials in the State Capitol.

Farwest County

FW_1 Ranked most responsible for initiating the Farwest project was FW_1, the state senator resident in Farwest County. This office, with its unusual extra-community access into state and regional legislative arrangements, was even more meaningful in that the senator was noted for his association with the Governor and his seniority in the state Senate. In addition, his legislative office had effected the passage of social legislation in the state dealing with the development of district hospitals. About the legislative office of FW_1 had developed an imagery in Farwest County that added a special capacity for influence. As one informant put it, "After all, there can't be much wrong with a fellow that comes from [another state] to [Farwest], becomes a successful newspaperman, goes to the legislature at 27, then to the Senate, and becomes a close friend of the Governor." The previous ownership of a local newspaper was reported to have provided FW_1 with "a lot of friends and a lot of contacts" in Farwest County.

It should be pointed out carefully that the constituted rights of the office of state senator, with resulting authority, were not directly relevant to decision-making in Farwest County. However, this position invoked a positive imagery of influence and provided an advantageous access into legislative arrangements both within Farwest County and on the state level. In addition, FW_1 had maintained an active interest and participation in the affairs of Farwest County, especially through speaking engagements before county organizations. Because of positional and influence elements, he was known to work closely with the Farwest County governing body, the Board of Supervisors. As one informant put it, "He is very close with the county officers and I believe that he was influential in appointing the Board of Directors for the Hospital District."

FW_2 The participant ranked second by Farwest County informants was "old family". His father, a Polish migrant, settled in the county as a young man. It must be reported that FW_2 held no offices, at least of the formal political type or of prestiged associations. In fact, there was general agreement that his participation in local affairs had been at a minimum and that his access into the associational life of the county, Champ, and Marino had never developed. But one positional element was important. He was legal consultant to the prominent lumber interests of Farwest County. In addition, this position had made him a wealthy man, and he was reputed to be the highest individual taxpayer in the county.

For the purposes of hospital decision-making, FW_2's position, although not providing the capacity of authority in any constituted form, provided a wide range of state and federal contacts. These extra-community relationships which brought him into a working relationship with the state senator, FW_1, had influenced FW_2 into full participation in the project, first as a member of the Hospital District Board of Directors, and eventually as chairman. The following comment perhaps best represents those made of the advantageous elements contained in the legal consultant position held by FW_2.

"His outside contacts benefited us most, especially with federal agencies such as the Forest Service that he had worked with. He really took the responsibility, even took it from other members of the Board, and then would come back and give them an outline of what he had done. He wasn't too well known around here because he was never around—always off on some kind of state business for the lumber interests."

In conclusion, the position of FW_2 afforded a wide variety of extra-community access, coupled with low and infrequent access to intra-community agencies and associations, but through his relationship with FW_1 he was able to penetrate the structure of the county governing body.

FW_3 The third high-ranked participant in the Farwest project was an "old family" representative, a middle-aged mining and construction engineer. Again, the positional element of political or associational office was not related to the activity of FW_3 in Farwest County, although he was considered an active "community man," especially in the Grange and the Masons. Yet, he was appointed to the Hospital District Board of Directors and served as its first president (later succeeded by FW_2). This circumstance resulted from a previously established relationship with the state senator, a relationship based on the latter's definition of FW_3's range of proficiencies in construction engineering. General agreement prevailed on the part of the informants that he was the only man in the county qualified to supervise large-scale construction.

As earlier described, the initial step in the Farwest project was that of forming a county-wide Hospital District, whose directors would have specialized authority in hospital construction and maintenance. Although two of the four principal decision-makers were primarily involved because of specific proficiencies, the instrumentality of the Hospital District provided specialized authority for decision-making. The Hospital District Board became a parallel authority agency to that of the County Supervisors. The offices of this new agency embodied the capacity of authority regarding hospital affairs. In other projects there was initially a hospital committee or board, but legitimacy depended on the constituted governing bodies that made the appointments. In Farwest County, the Board was not only a Hospital Board to manage the affairs of the hospital, *per se*, but it represented a constituted instrumentality, the Hospital District. Throughout the duration of the hospital-getting project in Farwest County, decisions were to be made within such a framework. Consequently, after the offices were filled with men possessing what were construed as essential skills and competences, decision-makers had the added capacity of newly-constituted authority. Such was the case with FW_3.

FW_4 A fourth active participant in the Farwest hospital project was a young osteopathic physician, aged 32, who practiced in Crossroads, the small community in which the original meeting for a hospital occurred. The leader of a small professional osteopathic group in the county, he was also a member of the County Board of Supervisors. Notwithstanding the circumstances that FW_4 was a newcomer to the county, informants described him as "a rising young man in county affairs." Most important, however, for the decision-making process in this project was his incumbency in the office of supervisor.

Earlier cited was an observation that the problem for the Farwest project was that of articulating two parallel agencies of authority. FW_4 assisted by attending the frequent meetings of the Hospital District Directors which, in effect, meant that the Board of Supervisors was represented. Throughout the course of the project, one of the contained oppositions was that of the osteopathic physicians, and FW_4 became active in their behalf when there was a threat that osteopaths would be excluded from practice in the new hospital. That the opposition was contained until a state ruling removed the threat is undoubtedly due to the supervisor office held by FW_4 and the simultaneous cooperation of the Board of Supervisors. The office of supervisor made it possible for FW_4 legitimately to attend Hospital District Board meetings, and to contribute his proficiencies as a medical man.

In contrast to the previous studies, decision-makers FW_1, FW_2, and FW_3 formed a loose friendship group; and the initiation of the project by FW_1 led to the participation of the other two. The major characteristics of this "relationship set" were a control of strategic access into extra-community arrangements and a community image of proficiencies in hospital development, i. e., legal knowledge and architectural and construction technology.

Norwest County

NW_1 As described in a previous chapter, the initiation of the Norwest project came from the mayor of Norwestville, not before the town council, but in the Norwestville Lions Club. Although it might be assumed that the office of mayor included certain prescribed rights for project initiation, the particular office did not appear to be so construed. NW_1 initiated from the position of a man viewed as "public-spirited," tending to link the Norwestville and out-county interests (as a rancher-businessman), and as an active participant in the town associations, especially the Lions Club.

NW_1, middle-aged and a representative of "old pioneer" group of families, was perceived by most informants as the chief benevolent figure in civic enterprises. General agreement prevailed that over a period of time he could be expected to make two major contributions to such enterprises: (1) "helping to get things started," and (2) contributing substantially to financial requirements because of his relatively wealthy economic position. The playing of the "initiating role" was undoubtedly facilitated by the political influence of being mayor, with subsequent access to the county governing body.

Note should be taken here of the first instance in project initiation of a formal political office oriented to the jurisdiction of a municipality rather than to the county. Norwest is the only project in which a municipal governing office was represented at the initiation of the project. In Southeast County, a municipal office was represented in later stages of the project, and in Midstate County the most critical opposition came from a town councilman.

Thus, Norwest provides an example in which initiation originates in the town as a sub-grouping, and in which the initiating role was linked to a municipal poltical official.

NW_2 The selection of NW_2 for participation in the Norwest project was made through an established friendship relationship with NW_1, the initiator. It was justified on the grounds of proficiencies for hospital construction. No political or associational offices were held. Such proficiencies were linked to his position as an executive in a currently important oil products industry in Norwest County. This executive position made for wide extra-community contacts for NW_2 but limited relationships in the immediate vicinity of Norwest County. Indeed, NW_1 reported, "I told (NW_2) he had to be active in the hospital project because the county had been good to him and this was a chance to repay it."

NW_2, considered a newcomer to Norwest County, shared with NW_1 a wealthy economic position. Early in the project a Hospital Board was appointed, with the advice of NW_1, by the Board of County Commissioners. Although the Hospital Board had less authoritative jurisdiction than the District Board of Farwest County, the entrance of NW_2 into its presidency simplified extra-community access for frequent negotiations with state and other officials. As one informant put it, "The time and effort which he gave to the hospital project would have amounted to $5,000 or more."

NW_3 Ranked as one of the four most active persons was a Norwestville businessman who enjoyed the community-wide image of "a good organizer." This talent had been exercised in the Norwestville Lions Club and, more recently, in the Chamber of Commerce. The important office here, in addition to previous official duties in the Lions Club, was the chairmanship of the county Republican Committee. Thus, he was locally considered as politically influential, though not in the formal sense, in municipal, county, and other political affairs. It was NW_3 who served on the exploratory committee appointed by the Lions Club and who later became a member of the Hospital Board. From this point, recalling that the Norwest project was characterized by an extensive mobilization of the associational life of the county, a division of labor occurred between NW_3 and NW_2. The latter, with wide extra-community access, assumed the role of negotiator with outside officials. NW_3 performed an organizing function within the county, especially in regard to fund-raising activities. These operations developed both from the Hospital Board and the Lions Club. Especially was this true in periods of emergency.

These three participants in the Norwest project formed the "inner circle" of decision-making. Although a great number of town and out-county representatives participated actively, these three appear centrally important. To ascertain a fourth from the rankings of the informants and the interpolation of analysis has proven difficult. The reason is the singular inter-play between the above three men, representing the Hospital Board and the Lions Club. This interaction led to a variety of Norwestville businessmen playing brief roles in the details of hospital development, with a continuing strong representation of the Lions Club. However, NW_4 must be cited briefly, in that he was the one member on the Hospital Board solely representing the out-county ranching industry.

NW_4 A member of the Hospital Board, NW_4 was the son of a prominent "old family," long involved in the ranching industry of Norwest County. He had completed law school and, rather than establish practice, had returned to Norwest County to assist the family in its enterprises. NW_4 was selected for the Hospital Board for two reasons: (1) He possessed a source of legal knowledge believed to be necessary in a hospital project; and (2) he represented directly the isolated and dispersed areas of the out-county. Although he held no offices except his Board membership, it should be noted that NW_4 was selected by a blending of two characteristics, family position and skill. This pattern, as the above treatment attempts to demonstrate, has been frequently employed.

NW_4 was not a part of the "relationship set" enjoyed by the other three high-ranked participants. Yet, initiation came from the "relationship set" of previous informal and friendship content, with the initiating role taken by a political official operating outside the political context. The difference is that the office represented was a municipal rather than a state one, and the similarity is that in both projects the initiating political officials were outside the county governing group. Another similar pattern is found. Following initiation, the "initiator" proceeded to involve what was to become perhaps the most important participant in each instance, an individual lacking a history of local participation but possessing proficiencies construed as essential to the pursuit of the hospital project.

Noreast

NE_1 The exclusively high-ranked participant in the Noreast hospital project had never held municipal or county political office. However, his control of offices in high-ranked associations was almost complete. NE_1 was vice-president of the Hospital Board, an office into which he had intentionally placed himself rather than in the presidency. The explanation was: "I have always, since my college days, preferred to be the No. 2 man. When there are troubles, everyone goes after the No. 1 man, which gives you enough time to decide what to do." Both the Presbyterian Church and the Noreast Rotary Club gave important associational support to the hospital project, and NE_1 was the presiding official in the former and a past official in the latter.

However, the pyramiding of the associational structure in Noreast centered in the Noreast Club, and it was there that all of the four selected decision-makers played important roles. Although not holding office at the time of the study, NE_1 was considered the "prime mover," as one informant stated, of the Club in that he had joined with NE_2 in its organization some 20 years previously. The following excerpted comments indicate some of the positional imagery supplied by Noreast informants.

"He has been on the Hospital Board for a long time, and always worked hard for the hospital . . . has been connected with the hospital for a long time . . . has held the Presbyterian Church together . . . never likes to take offices if someone else will take them, for he prefers to be the man behind the man . . . is the top man in (Noreast) for everything."

NE_2 The second high-ranked participant, with NE_1, formed a symbolic "behavioral set." Since the organization of the Noreast Club, the two, through community expectations, were regarded as "the team" in community affairs. Independently wealthy, NE_2 was noted for the time he spent in metropolitan centers handling the affairs of his extensive investments. Consequently, the extra-community access which he had was unparalleled by the others who joined with him in the project. Like NE_1, he had been a past officer of the Rotary Club, the co-founder of the Noreast Club with NE_1, and was brought into the Hospital Board by NE_1 to serve as president. In addition, NE_2 had served as a director of the Noreast bank and was noted for the contribution he made to its financial circumstances. He had recently reciprocated with NE_1 by introducing him into a directorship of the Bank.

The Board of Directors for the bank was considered strategic in regard to civic projects of finance, in that the incumbents had full knowledge of the financial affairs of the community. The foregoing offices held by NE_2 should indicate that, although his residence was on his large country estate, he entered into local affairs through the city of Noreast. Note the following excerpted comments.

"He was a central figure . . . he really has wide acquaintances and influence, wide contacts . . . he has a wider perspective than most local people, not only in business ability but on his station in life . . . really mixed up in a lot of things, leader in the Boy Scouts, past president of the Rotary Club, started the Noreast Club, and a strong president of the Hospital Board."

NE_3 The third-ranked participant represents a similar pattern of offices held. Having developed an extensive vegetable brokerage business, he, too, was noted for wide contacts throughout the state and region. His occupational position, together with his directorship in the Noreast bank, had made him the central figure in arranging credit for the farmers of Mary County. As several informants reported, "There isn't a single farmer in Mary County that does not know him, and he knows eveything about their financial condition." A common pattern of obtaining credit on the part of farm people was first to seek out NE_3, before contacting the bank, with the implication that his approval or disapproval was needed prior to approaching the bank.

NE_3 was a strong member in the Noreast Club, and a past president and extra-community participant in the Lions Club. A few years previously, when the Noreast Presbyterian Church was financially and organizationally unstable, NE_1 encouraged NE_3 to "come into" the church. As one informant put it, "[NE_1] brought [NE_3] into the church, his profanity and all, and had him help keep the church together." The following excerpted comments may indicate the public image regarding the station of NE_3.

"He has contacts with the farmers that not even farmers have . . . nobody can call so many people by their first names . . . has wide connections in both the town and the rural areas . . . quite an influential director of the Noreast bank . . . helped [NE_1] to get the Presbyterian Church on its feet."

NE_4 The fourth-ranked participant in the Noreast project was involved in the development partially on the basis of positional elements. His important and in some ways crucial office was highly relevant to the type of fund-raising project sponsored in Noreast. He was the president of the Noreast bank. Middle-aged, a newcomer to the community by fifteen years of residence, and without the advantageous economic position of the previous three, NE_4 possessed a history of having joined with the three in numerous community ventures. Constant interaction was maintained through his central position with the directors of the bank, and he had served as the business manager of the Noreast Club for several years. Active participation was maintained in the Rotary Club with NE_1 and NE_2.

NE_4 was noted in the community for his success with organizing previous campaigns, especially during the period of World War II. Consequently, he was seen by the other three as needed "for his administrative and organizational experience." As explained by the other three, his position was symbolically important in the pursuit of a fund-raising project, i.e., "we could hardly go into this sort of thing if the bank president was against us." Nevertheless, two of the other three high-ranked participants believed that it would have been possible to accomplish the task if this had happened. That such an event did not occur reveals the important distinction of the Noreast decision-making process—that the centrally important decision-makers were linked informally through an extensive array of reciprocal obligations.

At one point was the matter of position confused in the public image with the resources and proficiencies of influence commensurate with the office held. As one informant stated, "NE_4 kowtows to [NE_2] by going along on things, and 'apes' him in the Noreast Club because of money. People resent a person collecting money when he can't give it himself." Another said, "He probably pledged himself for the rest of his life in order to keep up on the money giving." The contribution which he made to the project was actually one of strategy in encouraging financial contributions, both by organization and by appeal. One statement perhaps indicates best the conclusions drawn from an analysis of the case materials: "The place where he (NE_4) really counted was because of his knowledge of the financial structure of the community, which came from his being a banker. However, because he is a banker, he is limited as such in the community."

These comments of the offices held by NE_4 demonstrate, together with previous comments, that the four decision-makers form a "symbolic set" in that certain positional elements are held in common and that historical obligations and shared experience in public affairs informally secured the relationship. Although a similar structure began to evolve in the Farwest project, and was seen again in Norwest, its extensive development is best seen in the Noreast project.

The Top Twenty

OBTAINING a hospital required more than the easy agreement of doing good for one's own home town. It was "sticking one's neck out." The people who did were, for the most part, neither farmers, social workers, nor doctors. They were the people who knew about dollars and banks and bookkeeping. They were the people who knew about the wealth of the community and, for the most part, possessed it. Ten of the twenty high-ranked participants were considered among the wealthiest families of the community. The other ten were moderately well-to-do. Fourteen of the ten were either "old family" or "near old family." Being male, being wealthy, and being of early residence in the community was a favorable position from which community leaders entered the hospital-getting process.

In the Norwest and Noreast projects, women played important auxiliary roles. Yet, administering decisions is different from making them. For the hospital projects employed in the present study, men made the original decisions and many others helped to carry them out. From the vantage point of the decision-making process, there is little doubt that small community hospital development under the provisions of Hill-Burton legislation has been essentially a male activity.

Apparent in every case were local definitions of the "need for responsible persons" in the collection of extensive financial resources. Perhaps it is not surprising that the men of the "inner circles" of decision-making are largely found in the maturity of middle age. Seventeen of the top 20 were between the ages of 40 and 60. But one was above 60 and only two under 40. One can only surmise that to become a political official in a local governing body, or to possess reputation for financial and legal skills, time is needed, which is reflected in age.

The top 20 were generally active in the associational life of the community or county. It is striking, indeed, that 16 of the 20 enjoyed a free and easy entrance into the organized ways of the community and, frequently, into the affairs of state and region. For the most part, the top 20 were the men who go to meetings, serve on committees, belong to almost every club in town, and complain that "they never have an evening at home." The evidence reveals that the complaint is correct. But because they are not at home, communities go about getting hospitals.

Yet, a few of the top 20 had not previously entered into the local arrangements for solving community problems. Where this occurred, a substitute attribute was possessed. The substitute was either special proficiencies deemed necessary in the hospital project or a wide acquaintanceship with people and places beyond the community.

County or municipal governing offices were irregularly represented in the intensively studied projects. In Southeast County each of the high-ranked participants was politically sensitive; of the four, one held the centrally important office of probate judge and another the office of councilman in Carlin, the county seat. In contrast, the Noreast project had no formal governing offices involved at all, and no governing bodies were related to the project. In both Midstate and Farwest Counties, governing officials were involved, but the incumbents initiated the projects outside the related political contexts. In Norwest County, the initiation of the project was performed by a municipal official, the mayor of Norwestville, but it was addressed to the associational life of the community rather than to governing agencies.

The relation of high-ranked participants to the respective hospital service areas differed. In the Southeast and Farwest projects, participants resided in the out-county rather than in the town site for the hospital. In Midstate County they consistently and completely resided in the site community. For Norwest, they represented both the out-county and the site community, which was true of Noreast, which exhibited a stronger identification with the site community.

Two kinds of roles may be found among the top 20 participants. Each may be constructed around an occupation. The first type forms a professional profile: a middle-aged, professional person, representing either an old established family or a newcomer to the community, classified in the middle income bracket, possessing average contacts outside the community in state, regional, and national circles, and with little history of holding office in local governing agencies. The second type forms a self-employed businessman or employed-executive profile, tending to represent an old or well established family in the community, belonging to the more wealthy group, residing in the town which serves as the site for the hospital, maintaining extensive activity in community associations of prestige, possessing contacts with persons and organizations both within and without the community, having no history of participation in governing offices and, finally, falling in the middle-aged bracket.

In some parts of the United States, the profiles would be expected to alter. In the Southeast project, the profile altered to include two incumbents of local governing offices. In the Midstate project, the professional pattern predominates, although including certain political offices as well as the self-employed businessman. The professional profile recurs in the Farwest case. In the Norwest project, the profile veers sharply toward the businessman-employed executive type which is seen at its fullest development in the Noreast project. In Noreast there was a total exclusion of the governing official so characteristic in the Southeast case.

XI. THE RESOURCES OF INFLUENCE

THE ADVENT of a hospital is, in one way, an energizer of social change in the small community. The stability of the small community is interrupted by new arrangements for satisfying community health needs. The emergence of a hospital campaign brings forth members of the community to assume the responsibilities required by the satisfaction of need. Participants in the hospital-getting process are drawn largely from certain stations in local life. Every high-ranked participant in the present projects "counted for something" because of offices and stations of believed importance which he held in his community. Every centrally important participant in the hospital project emerged from a background of offices held, and of family, status, and kinship positions which often rendered special advantage.

Still, position alone was not a sufficient platform from which to provide leverage for the hospital-getting process. Each participant had a history of dealings with his fellows which conditioned a community image of his capabilities. Because the active participant frequently symbolized, in the public eye, the values by which the community is unified, he was granted permission to make legitimately the necessary decisions in the hospital-getting process.

This chapter details briefly those major resources of influence possessed by high-ranked participants in the process of hospital acquisition. Although the focus will be on the resource, attention will be given to both the perceptions and the images of each community-at-large with regard to certain participants, and to certain contrasts among and within the five hospital projects studied intensively.

Wealth

No ATTEMPT was made to obtain exact evidence of wealth possessed by the high-ranked participants. However, the judgments of the informants placed each participant in a relative economic position within the community. At least ten of the 20 high-ranked participants in the five projects were in the high-income bracket of the community. The remaining ten participants fell no lower than the middle-income bracket, and of these, some would classify in the middle to high-income range.

In three of the projects, two of the four high-ranked participants were considered among the most wealthy men of their respective communities or counties—Southeast, Norwest, and Midstate. For the remaining two projects, at least one of the four high-ranked men represented the wealthiest group in the community.

The first dimension of wealth in the decision-making process was the manner by which it was obtained. The inheritance of wealth seemed to provide an uncertain ingredient of influence. The crucial distinction became the manner in which inherited wealth was employed for civic improvement. For example, the third-ranked participant in Southeast County was highly regarded for carrying on the long family tradition of public-spirited distributions of wealth obtained from large holdings of land. Almost legend in Southeast County was the tale of this family's ownership of a Carlin bank, which, with the coming of the depression, collapsed. As reported locally, the bank patrons were reimbursed from the family fortunes. The evaluation of the community-at-large was simply that "they have made a lot of money, but they use it to help rather than to hurt."

A minority of informants were disturbed that the second-ranked participant of Noreast, the wealthy gentleman-farmer, had achieved wealth by the easy route of family inheritance. It was said, "When you are a native of the community and your father leaves you a lot, this makes a lot of difference in the way people feel about you." Others exclaimed, "He has lots of money, which means that you can get away with a lot and people will 'kowtow' to you." However, the majority of informants agreed that "he was able to give freely of time and money," "he could appeal to other people with money merely by saying how much he gave," "he was able to work aggressively with the high-income folks," and "you have to find men with time and money in a project like building a new hospital."

Similar evaluations failed, however, to characterize all wealthy participants in the projects. The highest-ranked participant in Southeast County was held to be "a man who worries about little things when it comes to money." Discussed the length and breadth of Southeast County was the instance of his new farm pond, but "he won't allow a soul to fish in it, not even his own father." As they would say in Southeast County, "How do you like that for bein' cold-blooded?" Contrastingly, the second-ranked participant of Noreast was the subject of such comments as, "When he goes to a church supper, you will always find something extra under his plate when the supper is over."

For all five projects, access was gained to persons and agencies outside the community by one possessing great wealth, as judged by his community. Thus, the pattern of career and occupation tended to be linked to the accumulation of wealth, providing operational access to extra-community situations which were deemed essential for getting a hospital.

The possession of wealth enabled certain strategies to be utilized in the decision-making process. In fact, wealth frequently made strategy necessary. In Norwest County, men of wealth approached others of wealth, and "collected $17,000 of pledges without going off the Main Street of Norwestville." Initiators of the project in Noreast were prepared in advance to provide any deficit in the fund-raising campaign. Admission of this made possible the involvement of other high-ranked participants. The entire strategy of Southeast County, involving the large landowners and the possessors of great wealth, centered about the centralization of wealth in the Black Belt. Not to be overlooked in this recapitulation is the uncertain initiation of the Mid-state project by one lacking wealth, but insisting on the efficacy of a voluntary fund-raising campaign. Throughout the five projects, the belief was that "you can't ask for another person's dollar without doing at least as well, yourself."

In these ways, then, the resource of wealth entered into the decision-making process. A view of the high-ranked participants indicates that the possession of wealth was conditioned by the public image of its use in civic improvement, by the manner in which strategy was made possible or necessary by the locus of wealth, and by the fact that wealth alone may be bargained for, negotiated over, and transacted in the hospital project.

Respect

RESPECT is a deference value—an accorded valuation of intrinsic personal qualities. The evaluations by both the steering group and the community-at-large of the person decide the extent to which the ingredient of respect may be "put to work" in the decision-making process. Respect is the greatest resource gained in the dealings of the decision-maker with his fellows. Each high-ranked participant brought to the hospital-getting process some record of evaluated interpersonal behavior.

In Southeast County two sets of expectations conditioned the resource of respect—those of the Black Belt and the "hill country." Family position, stemming from the "old family that came from South Carolina," or the "poor country cousins" of the hill country, conditioned the respect image, depending on the vantage point of the viewer. Since the Black Belt contained the dominant group, the respect image was altered in its favor.

Informants in the Southeast project referred to the highest-ranked worker as "one of the poor country cousins and thus you can expect a narrow streak sooner or later." In the Black Belt the composite image was: "Oh! He made a lot of money up north, but he turned out to act like a big shot." "He was a big businessman and you might say that he likes to be boss and tell people what to do." "He has all his land posted and I don't post an acre of mine. You can't do things like that down here." "Everything he has done has rubbed people the wrong way, and he was even defeated politically in his own community because he can't get along with his neighbors and even his kinfolk." "He is a first-impression fellow, he dwarfs everything and everyone else, and his thought is the principal thought." As one informant put it in summary fashion, "You wonder why such a man was the chief one in the hospital. Why, he doesn't carry much weight, but when he gets blocked, he comes back and fights and fights. Add to this his organizing ability and the fact that he was president of the Farm Bureau—and he was in."

The third-ranked participant in Southeast County provided a contrast. The composite image would be: "Everybody likes him and his brother." "He is the richest man in the county but to see him you would never know it." "All he does is speak to a few people and soon everybody is for the idea." "He never tries to run things, since he is a real worker and doesn't have to be a big cheese." Even in the "hill country" informants stated, "His influence is personality and he is just as nice to one with a dime as a millionaire." "He would enjoy himself with a poor man as well as with anyone else." "He could have stopped the whole thing, but he is too refined and educated for that."

A second respect evaluation dealt with community judgments of intellectual capacity. This evaluation was especially acute in Southeast County where the theme of "education and refinement" was employed in status differentiations between the Black Belt and the hilly areas. Hence, the second probate judge received the following image: "He is radical, honest, and ignorant." "He's a country boy, not very educated, but means well." "He had no opportunity for education and is not as capable as the (other participants)." "He is really not educated for a job like that but he carried it out all right." "The others (participants in addition to the probate judge) were of a higher type, which goes back to one's family, being better raised, better educated, and thinking more in the future." "He didn't have what it takes in the Black Belt—class." Even informants in the "hill country" agreed, but with somewhat more compassion: "He was the one who really caused the hospital." "He is awfully abrupt and has little education, but has a mighty big heart." "He is radical but would make a good judge ten years from now."

The third-ranked participant in the Southeast project received an evaluation considerably different: "His family wealth meant that he didn't have to be interested in education, but he attended two universities with a good record." "Because of his family background and education, he is deep." "People respect him for his forward-looking way, since he went out for the hospital even though it was going to cost him several hundreds of dollars a year." "He is the kind of man who can tell you the straight truth and not make himself stand out."

A third evaluation of participants was concerned with respect gained by the sharing of the decision-making function. In Noreast numerous references were made to the first-ranked participant: "He will work hard at giving the job and the credit to someone else." "He always 'weaves' people into a community project." "He is very clever at handling people, but never takes the credit." "During the depression he would buy a poor kid a pair of shoes, but no one would ever know about it." "He can be hard-headed, he can be tough, but he does everything in a quiet way." "He is a good old solid community man and chances are that you would never know that he is behind a project."

Other evaluations dealt with the importance of one "having made his own way and having become successful through hard work"; and of possessing highly specialized knowledge or skill in subject matter such as law or finance. The high-ranked participants characteristically possessed the resource of respect. Although most evaluations were on the positive side, projects except Farwest did have at least one participant with a negative respect evaluation. In Southeast County two participants received a negative evaluation. That this could occur concurrently with a high rank of importance in securing the hospital is explained by the possession of other resources and proficiencies, and by incumbency in offices of local county and municipal government.

"Morality"

THE RESOURCE of "morality" occurs with evaluations by the community of a decision-maker who "can do no wrong." Respect deals with evaluations of the history of the individual's interpersonal relationships; "morality" deals with evaluations of what he stands for. The image of "morality," or moral rectitude, failed to materialize as an important resource brought to the decision-making process by the high-ranked participants.

The only distinctive image of "morality" was seen in Noreast, in the person of the highest-ranked participant, the printing company owner. The cue was an exclamation made in Noreast, "He is the personification of our community." To explain this statement is to explain the resource of "morality." As one informant put it, "Some people worry only about the goal, and they will step on people to reach it; others are so afraid of people that they never get any place for fear of hurting someone," and "Mr. [NE₁] makes sure that we reach the goal, but you have the feeling that he never considers it more important than the people."

In the Noreast project, one newspaper publisher was opposed to the new hospital. After planning active opposition through the press, he failed to continue. His explanation was simply that "if Mr. [NE₁] was to be in it, no opposition could seriously prevail . . . . he is the sort of man that no one would believe could do any wrong." Noreast legend has it that the printing company owner was earlier responsible for settling a local strike of workers. The local interpretation was, again, that . . . . "you can't find a person who can withstand his ethical approach and his basic goodness." In addition, self and public images provided the interpretation that his definition of civil responsibility dealt with being "a good Christian."

The negative images of respect in Southeast County contrast sharply with the emotional interpretations of this highest-ranked participant in Noreast. This contrast indicates the extent to which the Southeast project moved toward the hospital on the basis of local constituted authority; and the Noreast project's progress in the direction of the hospital on the basis of influence.

Success

THE RESOURCE of success deals with the expectation that a given person will always meet with success in local ventures. In addition, there is the added dimension of success in occupation or business. Study findings indicate that 11 of the 20 high-ranked participants possessed a distinct image of success in previous civic projects and in business; four possessed only an image of personal success; three were awarded an image of success only in community enterprise. Two participants failed to receive the success image.

In Southeast County the interpretation placed on the successful incumbency of the highest-ranked participant as president of the Farm Bureau was that of "his success as a business executive up north." Although the means employed by the Farm Bureau president to achieve the hospital evoked a negative image of respect, there was belated admission that his "hard-driving business experience" was the central factor in effecting the new hospital. A distinctive contrast of Southeast with Midstate is provided by the local explanation of difficulties in the latter project: "The real trouble was that the men in charge of the hospital project had no experience in such things and had never proved themselves in community work."

In the Farwest project the initiator, a state senator, was credited with extraordinary achievement in legislative circles. Hence, no question was ever raised about his recommendations for, as several informants put it, "No one could question his knowledge of what was happening in the state capitol, and no one could forget how successful he had been in introducing social legislation to improve the conditions of California." In addition, the third-ranked participant in Farwest was believed to be "the most successful construction engineer around . . . . if he didn't know about building a hospital, the rest of us were sunk." In similar fashion, the initiator of the Norwest project was credited with having "put a lot of things across in the community." The second-ranked participant in Norwest, with no record of community achievement, was known and credited throughout the entire Northwest as a successful executive and, as some said, "truly a builder."

For Noreast, all four high-ranked participants enjoyed an image of publicly credited success. Especially was this true of the two men who had "put the church on its feet and a lot of other things, too." Informants believed that fund drives in Noreast received their greatest support from the printing company owner, ranked highest by informants. As one stated, "Why, he was in my office yesterday and I'll bet he had three or four different tickets in his pocket to sell for some benefit." Another said, "It is a standing joke of mine with him, that when I see him I ask him what he is trying to sponsor now." Even the fourth-ranked participant, the banker, with an uncertain possession of resources, was believed to have "put the community on top by heading up the bond drives during the war."

In these ways, either personal or community success may enter the decision-making process. It should be noted that the resource of personal success, if related to relevant financial, organizational, and technical skills, may accord a favored position to participants without a previous successful achievement in civic enterprise. As earlier evidence suggests, one reason for utilizing the resource of success in decision-making is to contain opposition that might otherwise flare into active opposition.

Access

THE RESOURCE of access may operate in the decision-making process in two directions: the access to one's own community through membership and office in community associations of prestige which are relevant to the respective project; and access to agencies and other arrangements outside the community which are, again, of relevance to the proposed project.

Sixteen of the 20 high-ranked participants were members or officers of those associations within the community which informants believed could have initiated action toward a new hospital. Of the 20 participants, only two belonged to a single association believed capable of initiating the project. Only two of the 20 participants lacked membership or officership in any such associations. In both instances, however, participants possessed extraordinary skill or unusual access into outside administrative and legislative agencies.

In each of the five projects one person assumed the role of expediting technical details with outside agencies. This person, by occupation and previous experience, enjoyed sufficient contacts with outside sources to insure the facilitation of such technical details. In Southeast County the probate judge—the "ambassador" for county affairs—secured financial assistance from state agencies. In Midstate County, the Larch druggist made the trips to the state capitol since "he was a friend of the Governor." For Farwest County the legal consultant for the lumber industry employed his business contacts of many years. Informants stated, "His outside contacts benefited us most."

In Norwest County arrangements outside the community were handled by the oil company executive. As he said of himself, "I have been in a lot of business meetings, and I was not afraid of getting on the 'phone and calling the people who could help us out." In Noreast, extra-community arrangements were developed by the two highest-ranked participants. One, the wealthy gentleman-farmer and financier, followed his business contacts throughout the state; the other, the printer, employed his extensive connections with hospital agencies and consultants.

The importance of the resource of access to the hospital-getting process then was twofold: (1) major participants actually controlled, through membership and officership, those community associations whose approval of the project, in the public eye, undergirded the initiation of the project; and (2) there was at least one role in each project which dealt exclusively with negotiations outside the local community. The person who assumed this role was selected because of extraordinary connections gained through occupation and business.

Obligation

THE RESOURCE of obligation is but one segment of the interpersonal history which each key figure brought to the decision-making process. The extent of obligation owed to such a participant, either by other key figures or the community-at-large, is a resource of distinctive advantage in obtaining approval and support for a new hospital. Obligation develops where the value is held that acts of goodwill, friendliness, and assistance place one in another's debt until they are repaid.

Felt obligation as a resource of influence varied within and between the five projects, with a strong contrast between Southeast County and Noreast. In Southeast County, there was no history of reciprocal obligations between the centrally important participants. In Midstate County the physician, "who had gone beyond the call of duty in practicing without a hospital," possessed a community-wide image of felt obligation.

In Farwest County the loosely grouped set of high-ranked participants had developed less through felt obligation among them, but more from the estimations of skill and proficiency which each possessed. However, the disposition of the Farwest state senator toward his home county had created throughout the county a general feeling of obligation. For Norwest County three high-ranked participants were reciprocally obligated through sharing in civic projects. But it is in Noreast that a "team" was a firm reality after 20 years of reciprocal assistance rendered in many ways by each of the four men to the others.

This history of reciprocal obligations must rest as the essential element individualizing the Noreast project. The following documented profile of obligatory relationships between the four high-ranked participants of Noreast bears testimony to this conclusion.

OBLIGATION OF:

NE$_1$ to NE$_2$: Both participants had been close friends for some twenty years. Each agreed that NE$_1$ had "introduced" NE$_2$ to the organized life of the city of Noreast. NE$_1$: "NE$_2$ makes a good president, and I have been getting him into those jobs for years."

NE$_1$ to NE$_3$: NE$_1$, when the Noreast Presbyterian Church was in precarious financial straits, called on NE$_3$ to join him—and the church—in a re-building task. As NE$_1$ put it, "I'll be grateful for a long time for the help NE$_3$ gave me at the church."

NE$_1$ to NE$_4$: During World War II, NE$_1$ was responsible for a number of bond sale drives. Believing himself to be lacking in organizational ability, he had called on NE$_4$ to devise the bond sale organizations. NE$_1$, a founder of the Noreast Club, defined his debt to NE$_4$ for the latter's handling of the Club's business affairs. NE$_1$ mused, "There has to be a work horse in every club."

NE$_2$ to NE$_1$: NE$_2$ quickly explained, "There are few men with whom I have been through so much with as NE$_1$."

NE$_2$ to NE$_3$: A variety of mutually advantageous business relationships had encouraged NE$_3$ to interest NE$_2$ in serving as a director of the Noreast bank. The directorship was the climax of NE$_2$'s participation in the affairs of Noreast, although his residence was in the out-county.

NE$_2$ to NE$_4$: NE$_2$ had served as the only president of the Noreast Club, while NE$_4$ had managed its business affairs. In addition, the directorship of the Noreast bank, supported by its president (NE$_4$), secured the entrance of NE$_2$ into Noreast civic affairs.

NE$_3$ to NE$_1$: In previous years NE$_3$ had cared for an invalided member of his family. As he stated: "For five years NE$_1$ visited him when everyone else in the comunity had forgotten about it. Why, if NE$_1$ told me to dig up the main street of Noreast, I would be out there doing it."

NE$_3$ to NE$_2$: NE$_2$ had secured the entrance of NE$_3$ into the Noreast Club, rendering it possible for NE$_3$ to engage in city affairs although a resident of the out-county.

NE₃ to NE₄: During the depression NE_3 undertook a precarious business venture. NE_4 was instrumental in negotiating a large loan, which
was repaid "with convenience." This event later led to NE_3
becoming a director of the bank. Informants reported NE_3
would not go along with a financial project if NE_4 failed to
approve it.

NE₄ to NE₁: NE_4, the bank president, could not compete with the other
    to NE₂: high-ranked participants because of a more uncertain family,
    to NE₃: status, and economic position. Due to his organizational ability,
and the obligations posed above, the three had invited him to
assume perfunctory roles in civic projects, thereby making it
possible for him to enter many arrangements of importance in
the city of Noreast.

That the "team" of Noreast had not been assembled by chance should be
evident. As earlier references have demonstrated, the high-ranked participation groups in Norwest and Farwest tended to have a degree of the Noreast
group's closeness, resulting in all cases from a mutually-shared history of
interpersonal relationships. In contrast, both Midstate and Southeast found
the incumbents of certain offices and positions moving from constituted
agencies and arranging themselves into alignments advantageous enough
for procuring a new hospital.

The obligation felt toward the high-ranked participants of Southeast
County was not that of individuals to each other, but that expressed by the
specific positions in Southeast County which each represented. The president of the Farm Bureau could depend on the support of the directors, especially after receiving their formal commendation for his service in strengthening the organization. In addition, the Farm Bureau president symbolized
to the members the growing obligation of that organization, already imple-
mented by hospitalization insurance, for the improvement of health facilities.

The second-ranked participant in Southeast County, the probate judge,
reaped the returns from political favors both within and without the county.
Many areas of Southeast County, especially those aligned with the incumbent
state administration, had received the probate judge's favors in the construction and maintenance of local roads. The strong position of the probate judge
in favor of the hospital was bolstered by the out-county representatives of
such favored areas. In this way, the probate judge, appointed to office by the
incumbent state administration, was able to employ the implied relationship
for gaining financial assistance in spite of the disfavor in which he was held
in the Black Belt.

The third-ranked participant, the large Black Belt landowner, automatically had at his disposal the votes of obligated workers on his estate. An
even more important obligatory tie, in this case, dealt with his symbolic position in the Black Belt. As Black Belt informants believed, "If anyone of us
stands for refinement and education, it is he." This, of course, imposed an
obligation on the participant as well as on the Black Belt. Then, too, the timing
of the Southeast project found this landowner in office as a director of the

Farm Bureau. Therefore, his symbolic position as a favored representative of the Black Belt could not be sacrificed by opposition to the hospital.

The fourth-ranked participant, the city councilman of Carlin, had influence with only one segment of the organized life in Southeast County, the educated classes of the county seat of Carlin. He had led the drives to support the two small colleges in the town, of great importance to the people of Carlin. This had enabled the schools' chief benefactor to attain the office of councilman, and to make plans to contest for the state legislature.

Felt obligation among the four high-ranked participants was almost nonexistent. They were politically aligned two against two on the issue of the incumbent state administration. The Farm Bureau president had been defeated for the office of probate judge without the support of the others. Only one of the four was a true representative of the Black Belt tradition. Two were, as viewed by the Black Belt, "poor country cousins." Only one was from an old family "that came from South Carolina." The others were relative newcomers. Said the Black Belt representative, of the probate judge: "Give him his due . . . . he first suggested the bond issue . . . . but . . . . he is a poorer educated judge than we've had before." Even a glimpse of the evidence suggests that the high-ranked participants of Southeast County lived in, and represented, sociologically distinct worlds. This circumstance had provided little opportunity to develop an interpersonal history of shared experience, especially that of mutually felt obligation.

The resource of obligation, then, as entered in the decision-making process, may have two forms. The first form deals with a diffused feeling of obligation on the part of the community, or some part of it, toward a key figure in procurement of the hospital. Further, the participant may feel obligation to the community. The highest-ranked participant of Noreast remarked, "If Noreast was going to get a new hospital, it was up to me to start something."

The second form consists of obligatory relationships, in various degrees, among the participants themselves. In Southeast County a constellation of offices and other positions made the decision-making function largely authoritatively effective. In Noreast, conversely, a history of sharing the decision-making function in civic affairs had produced an internally obligated circle of participants in the decision-making process.

Time

THE HOSPITAL project required extensive quantities of time. Since the project developed largely on the basis of voluntary efforts, the community-at-large was well aware of this ingredient of influence in community affairs. The entrance of the high-ranked participants into the hospital procurement process depended on a history of voluntary participation in civic affairs, itself a measure of time committed in the past. In most instances, it had been extensive. Just four of the 20 high-ranked participants contributed substantial time to the project because their occupations allowed it. Three of the five project initiators occupied offices which provided some remuneration for the time devoted to the hospital.

The resource of time was linked with other resources needed for the exercise of particular duties in the project. The most time-consuming duties were those of negotiation with officials of hospital and architectural agencies, both within and outside the community. In each instance where a specific participant assumed the duties of these negotiations, the resource of time was concurrent with the resources of wealth and extra-community access, and with the proficiencies of legal and financial skill.

For the Noreast project the resource of time was considered of great importance by the four high-ranked participants. The decision to employ a professional fund-raiser, as explained by the initiating participants, resulted from their belief that he could provide sufficient time to insure a successful fund-raising campaign. These key men were uncertain if their own occupations would allow the time to organize and conduct the campaign successfully. Hiring the professional fund-raiser was, in part, a way to subsidize the time that had to be committed by someone.

XII. PROFICIENCY AND INFLUENCE

PART OF the hospital-getting process was an exercise in skills and technology. Some knowledge of legal affairs simplified an approach to legislative bodies on many levels. In later stages of the project a stream of technical consultants entered the local community. Many participants with little previous experience in construction projects found themselves discussing the geology of construction sites, traffic flow within the hospital, and the specific designs for boiler rooms, laboratories, and sterilizing facilities. The hospital quickly became a problem of bonds, contracts, bids, hearings, and petitions. The men along Main Street frequently were required to rise to new heights of technical proficiency.

Reports of the 218 projects give evidence that persons of known proficiency were invited to assist the project. In many instances these persons had not before taken part in community affairs. Yet their proficiency was needed. The possession of proficiency in one or more areas of hospital technology opened the door for many into the decision-making process of building a new hospital.

Subject-Matter Competence

A MINIMUM previous knowledge of hospital operation and construction characterized the 20 high-ranked participants. Only two of the five projects were able to call on men with prior hospital experience. In Southeast County, the president and a director of the Farm Bureau had been concerned with the development of Blue Cross hospitalization insurance. This experience with Blue Cross brought them into contact with many of the potentialities of hospital services.

In Midstate County, none of the four most active participants possessed experience in hospital operation and construction. In Farwest County, one of the four main figures was involved because his profession was construction engineering. This was the subject of many comments: "He was one of the few in the county trained to perform the job of supervising the hospital construction." "He held respectable and responsible construction positions before this job." "They felt he was a good one to have on the Board because of his ability." "He is a good engineer."

For Norwest County, there was no hospital experience represented. The initiating mayor of Norwestville had, however, interested himself increasingly in the only private facility then operating in the county. This, as he reported, resulted in an appreciation of the minimum standards of hospital service. The mayor stated: "I would dream of the little hospital catching on fire some night and could picture them tossing people out of the window."

The Noreast project best represented the making of decisions on the basis of technical competence. This circumstance was due to the existence of a small operating hospital in the community, and the coinciding development of a hospital auxiliary. In Noreast, two of the four high-ranked participants were members of the existing hospital board. One had succeeded his father in the task. The "Twigs," the organized women's auxiliary, enabled knowledge of hospital affairs to be disseminated throughout the community. In addition, the civic affairs of Noreast were oriented favorably to health and welfare activities.

A high degree of technical competence in hospital operation and construction was shown by the highest-ranked participant in the Noreast project. Indeed, hospital operation had become an avocation for him. Of this, the community was aware. He had developed an extensive library on hospital operation and construction, and was noted for frequent attendance at hospital conferences, and for his negotiations with the Gately Regional Hospital Council. Informants consistently referred to his "hobby" of hospitals: "I relied a great deal on his knowledge of hospitals." "He has been looking at hospitals around for several years." "He always wants to know the facts, and always studies things out." This evidence, together with the presence of demonstrated subject-matter competence, provides the conclusion that the beginning of professionalism among laymen in community affairs was found only in Noreast.

In four of the five hospital projects a county bond issue secured funds for hospital construction. In each instance, attention to both enabling and restrictive legislation was required. State and federal agencies were legally involved in all five projects. In Midstate County crucial opposition to the project was cast in the form of a "remonstrance," a legal instrumentality. Only in Noreast was the project free of local legalities, excepting the formal receipt of funds from federal agencies and the Gately Regional Hospital Council.

Among each group of four high-ranked participants was found one role devoted largely to legalities. In Southeast County the probate judge provided the necessary legal skill. In Midstate county the circuit judge served as a consultant to the hospital sponsoring group and, in his own words, " . . . helped out wherever I could." By his assistance the remonstrance that immobilized the project was removed. In Farwest County, the legal consultant for the lumbering companies carried the bulk of legal responsibilities, and the state senator assisted in legal formation of the hospital district. In the Norwest and Noreast projects, legal details were assumed altogether by individual participants.

In the Southeast, Midstate, and Farwest projects the tasks of dealing with legalities were taken by individuals having either legal training or legal positions. For Norwest and Noreast, the tasks were taken by persons not in legal positions or possessing legal training. Instead, they were wealthy businessmen with extensive state and regional business experience.

Exercising Financial Skills

HOSPITAL procurement was also an exercise in financial planning, dealing, and strategy. Seventeen of the 20 high-ranked participants were successful businessmen or professional men in their respective communities.

Competence in finance went beyond successful experience in the business world. Circumstances often required the strategy of financial commitment. For example, in Southeast County the large landowners were the great holders of wealth, and the first step in the project became that of neutralizing the opposition of the landowners to any threat of higher taxes. After the large landowners had given approval, one could expect that the rank and file of the citizenry would believe that, "The landowners will suffer the most, so why not the rest of us?"

The first step in Midstate County was to justify an expensive project in "one of the poor areas of the state." The uncertain selection of fund-raising devices reflected, in part, some doubts about how to announce an expensive project in the face of beliefs that "taxes are too high." In Norwest County, a sum of $15,000 had to be raised voluntarily before a bond issue was legitimate. In Noreast, the initiation of the project was kept secret until the financial approachability of the community was thoroughly assessed. In frequent instances, there was need for a "go-between" to bargain both with the community and the outside agencies in reaching a satisfactory balance of financial contributions.

Rising construction costs made for under-estimation of hospital costs and consequent embarrassment to all five hospital boards. This usually called for alternative methods of financing, on the assumption that the community would resist successive use of the same fund-raising device. In Southeast County a sales tax followed a bond issue after the project was scaled down. In Midstate County there was absolute dependence on federal funds before the project could proceed. For Farwest and Norwest Counties, a reduction and revision in the estimates for the hospital occurred. There was much delay in Noreast until financial support was obtained from a health foundation.

Organizational Skill

ORGANIZATIONAL skill is defined as those abilities required in developing an organizational scheme, setting the scheme in motion, and dealing with the day-by-day details of operation. Two of the five projects, Norwest and Noreast, engaged in extensive organizational arrangements to gain consensus and raise funds.

Each of the 218 reporting projects was confronted with a need for some organizational work. This need came at differing stages, but no project escaped it. In Southeast County organization served the purposes of commitment, as the hospital committee was appointed by the probate judge. That the scheme did not backfire was due to the faulty estimation of the organizational abilities of the president of the Farm Bureau on the part of the large landowners.

149

In Midstate County organizational skill was conspicuously lacking. Since the chief problem of this project was one of articulating the two towns of Larch and Westville, it is revealing, indeed, that initiating participants did not concern themselves seriously with this task. Conversely, in Farwest County a full year was spent in the organizational details of establishing sponsorship. Special attention was given to interlocking the parallel structures of hospital sponsorship by an overlap of the offices in both.

One of the high-ranked participants in Norwest County was involved in the project precisely because he enjoyed a public image of being a "good organizer." It was this participant who decided, from time to time, the kind of organization required for specific fund-raising activities. He met the emergency of a quickly needed $21,000 by proclaiming, "We can't waste time on nickels and dimes," and proceeding to collect $1,000 pledges along the Main Street of Norwestville.

The Noreast project employed organizational skill most extensively. The design was to raise funds entirely by an organizational arrangement. The project was initiated in the belief that sufficient organizational ability was already vested in the community to complete the project. However, some concern developed that, once the plan was put in motion, motivational appeals might not be sustained. To forestall this, the key group decided that a professional fund-raiser could contribute motivational appeal and enough time to keep the plan sufficiently sustained. During the period of supervision by the professional fund-raiser, the bank president and the printer played staff roles in advising on organizational detail. One example was the near-appointment of a committee which was entirely made up of Presbyterians. Before the names of the committee were released to the press, the highest-ranked participant was able to obtain what he believed was a more equitable religious representation.

The professional fund-raiser of the Noreast project possessed remarkable organizational skill. For a period of three weeks the entire community lived in the grip of a short-range bureaucracy which required "that every person must have an office of responsibility and people under him." In this way, a project that had initiated from an informal group of four influentials became a highly organized and impersonal campaign. Details of the plan were impersonally considered. Hundreds of community residents, without previous experience in community affairs, became "division leaders," "captains," "committeemen," "workers," and "reporters."

Every speech and every argument in the appeal for funds was scrupulously reviewed and then worked out and taught to the participants. The following excerpts from the written instructions of the professional fund-raiser to the participants in an approaching campaign dinner are illustrative.

Since you are chairman, please briefly thank the workers and guests present for their attendance, and express a cordial welcome to all who have joined with us this evening.

You will please follow the program. Each speaker is definitely limited to an on-the-time basis. All speakers are asked to conform to this rule; then proceed to follow the program by calling on the persons enumerated.

As vice-chairman of this campaign, you should briefly review the pertinent facts pertaining to the hospital. We have a number of guests present and it would be well to lay a good foundation, so they will understand the needs of the hospital. Emphasize the following points:, etc.

When you conclude refer to the chairman and say something of this nature: "Mr. Chairman, you asked me to recruit an army to take the field . . . and I present this army of men and women to you . . . they are ready for action; they have demonstrated their interest and loyalty in the new hospital . . . ," etc.

Communication with the community was assured through organizational devices. After the meeting cited above, a report went to all the workers in the campaign and the organizations of the community. The following statement is an excerpt:

The marshalled cohorts of the (Noreast) Hospital have taken the field 650 strong . . . determined that $125,000—yes, $150,000—shall be raised to build a new hospital for the citizens of (Mary) County. They have what it takes . . . these workers . . . nearly 400 of them were present at the opening dinner . . . courage . . . determination and will power . . . they've got it and are going to put it to work. The "little ladies" under the leadership of Mrs. (Smith) made a fine showing. Our Generalissimo, Mr. (NE_2), did a fine job, DO YOU AGREE?

That this form of organization could possibly descend upon the community of Noreast was due in considerable part to the entrance of the professional fund-raiser. At the time of the study, informants agreed that the raising of funds without taxation had necessitated the employment of skill in community organization. That the exercise of such skill will be long remembered by the residents of Noreast is indicated by such comments as, "He (the professional fund-raiser) had a system second to none." "He was the maestro of the concert." ". . . put everything in proper relation and set the spark, tied it all together and set it going." ". . . never heard a person who could say so many words in five minutes, not what 'I' can do, but what the community can do."

This brief review will indicate that organizational skill was a widely distributed ingredient of influence among the 20 high-ranked participants, although the necessity for such skill varied among the projects. For the Southeast, Midstate, and Farwest projects, no organizational machinery involving the community- or county-at-large was employed; instead, associations and jurisdictional agencies were administratively articulated. In the Norwest and Noreast projects the residents of the respective service areas were activated by means of extensive organizational machinery. The tasks of organization were given to one or two persons, selected specifically for their "organizing ability." Organizational skill was utilized to the greatest extent in Noreast, where the initiators of the project employed a professional fund-raiser to devise an intensive campaign for funds. The professional fund-raiser was, in effect, an influential who was able to direct the project solely on the basis of proficiency.

Skill With Symbols

SKILL WITH symbols may be defined as the ability to recognize and to manipulate appropriate community symbols. A community hospital has inherent symbolic connotations, which were employed in gaining initial approval for the five projects. However, the phase in which symbol manipulation was most extensive was that of fund-raising.

The crucial problem in Southeast County was to commit the large landowners to an approval of the project, even though their individual reactions to the project might be negative. Most important was the Black Belt image, and the self-image, of the landowners as being "educated and refined." In the appointment of the hospital committee, the symbolic definition of the hospital as "a great step forward in Southeast County," and the "educated and refined" sentiments of the large landowners, were assumed to have identity.

For Midstate County no manipulation of symbols was initially directed at the disparate solidarities vested in two nearly autonomous towns of the county. This lack of organizational schemes and appeals to the entire county led to resistance by influentials of Westville. This, in turn, was interpreted as an attempted larceny by Larch. The leaders were never quite able to apprehend the sentiments of the divisive setting and, ruling out strategic organization or symbolic manipulation, depended upon legal instrumentalities. One use of symbol manipulation was the exploitation of the "overworked doctor" theme in Larch to gain the approval of the Larch community.

For Norwest County, the rationale for a new hospital, as put before the original meeting of the Lions Club, was premised on the theme that "no doctors will be forthcoming to the community without a hospital," and "we are in a critical condition without a physician." The case included a reference to the physician-son of a former doctor who, desiring to return to Norwest County, had stated, ". . . no doctor could be expected to practice in a community without some hospital facilities." The appeal to the Lions Club included references to recent crisis events in the existing private hospital. These involved persons known to all and made the need of a hospital seem urgent.

In Noreast the need for a hospital could have been met by other alternatives, i. e., an addition to the old hospital. This is one explanation of the secret assessment of the financial potential of the community by the professional fund-raiser. Gaining the approval of the Board for the old hospital was accomplished, in part, by references to the former Board president's "dream" of a new hospital, a symbol in itself. Thus, the memorial possibilities of the new hospital became evident to members of the Hospital Board.

The fullest expression of skill with symbols was exercised by the professional fund-raiser of the Noreast project. In addition to personal organizational skill, the professional fund-raiser flooded the community with materials designed to give the campaign bureaucracy the symbolic quality of a social movement. He provided sufficient communicative ties to make the short-lived organization a functioning system, impersonally distinct from the allegiances of normal community life.

A variety of symbols were manipulated by means of pamphlets, newspaper articles, speeches, and informal contact. Extensive use was made of appeals and slogans oriented to personal motivation: "What part are you playing in life?" "The measure of success is in terms of those unseen and intangible values that give human life meaning." "Your gift may mean a life restored." "Give a gift that keeps on giving." "We tend more and more in these latter years to look to the state to supply all our needs, but it would be a sorry day in America if the right and privilege of voluntary association for aid to the unfortunate were ever surrendered to the government." "Don't compromise with conscience." "Let the memory of Our Loved Ones be a Blessing to the Living." "Service and sharing, in charity and sympathy, in pity and mercy, these are the lasting things in life." "I could not ask for anything again, if I had not when asked been willing here to give my all to help my fellowmen, and pass along my share of human cheer."

Since the short life cycle of the campaign organization depended on the identification of its workers, certain symbols were devised to give the worker a feeling of importance in the activity and, also to provide the rules by which he might relate himself to fellow-workers. The following excerpt is taken from one of many pamphlets designed for this purpose: "As a sales representative of the cause, take inventory of yourself first . . . a good salesman must have pep . . . the world loves pep and is instantly drawn to anyone who has it . . . pep brings prestige, power, and perhaps most important—money . . . money . . . money for a new hospital." "Talk . . . think . . . and act with pep." "No matter what gems of wisdom—what pearls of information may exist inside that brain of yours—they are all likely to be wasted unless you dispense them with pep . . . pep is a religion . . . an ideal . . . and in actual practice, a powerful hypodermic." "Just to dwell on a good example of pep is to generate pep within yourself at once."

Small wonder that one informant exclaimed: "This was the greatest set of revival meetings any community ever had. Some of us have never been able to match the enthusiasm gained at that time." That such extensive organizational machinery and such a high symbolic content were evoked in Noreast may be explained partially by the complete lack in the hospital plan of constituted bodies of authority and legal instrumentalities for fund-raising. The devices employed in Noreast appear to be one way to control the sentiments of various publics found in a decision-making setting which functions on the basis of influence rather than authority.

Summary attention should be directed toward varied needs for the employment of skill with symbols. In three of the five projects, decision-making occurred within certain legally prescribed bodies which could, in turn, legitimately authorize legal instrumentalities to collect funds. In these same three projects early justification was based on definitions of acute need. However, in both Norwest and Noreast the relevance of constituted bodies of authority diminished and in Noreast were excluded altogether. Instead, one finds increasing organizational machinery and an increased exercise of skill with symbols.

The Legendary Personality

THE FIVE projects further revealed the importance of legend to influence. To the extent that many such legends are actually interpretations of personality eccentricities by relevant publics, they assist an understanding of the capacities for decision-making.

The initiator of the hospital in Southeast County had become a figure of legend because of his ability to "drive" people on a project in spite of their lack of enthusiasm; and, because, even with great wealth, he demonstrated a singular resistance to minute encroachments on his personal property. By far the majority of informants in Southeast County made comments about this, with the damaging interpretation that these characteristics resulted from years of experience in the North. It was said that, ". . . they may act that way up there, but it doesn't go over in the South."

Two high-ranked participants in the five projects had become legend in their respective communities through the eccentricity of non-conforming "boisterousness." In both instances, "boisterous" behavior in public affairs was interpreted as that of "being a real man that won't take 'no' for an answer." When informants were asked what this contributed to a community project, the response was: "The project may be a serious one, but you are bound to have some fun when he's mixed up in it." The following comments summarize the community image of one Farwest participant.

> "He plays hard and he works hard . . . he drank awfully hard but that made him one of the boys with a lot of people." "Boy, he could sure be sarcastic." "Some of the M.D.'s went to him and said that they wouldn't work in the hospital if the osteopaths were permitted to work in it. He told them right back that it didn't make any difference to him where they worked, and that he had never got any place by being choosey about where he worked." "You never knew what he was going to do next, which is one reason why people stood in awe of him." "Why, when he died, the whole Board was lost."

Then, there was the "court jester", as he was called, of Noreast. As he said, "You can't let the people take themselves too seriously." Numerous references were made to legend stories involving the profanity and brusqueness of this participant. As one informant put it, "He's a wild man, a real steamboat . . . fearless in collections . . . rough and ready, but an awful good fellow."

It was generally believed in Noreast that the effectiveness of another key man in dealing with others was that they could not cope with his "good-natured nervousness." One legend had it that to the extent that he was "nervous," to that extent was a new community project forthcoming. Repeated by a number of the informants was an event of labor-management negotiations over a local strike. These informants believed that the particular man of legend settled the strike by appearing at the headquarters of the negotiations and proceeding to baffle the negotiators (as reported, by "nervousness") until a solution was found.

In Southeast County negative images and negative legends did not remove the incontrovertible fact that the decision-maker was the incumbent of an office of authority. Conversely, in Noreast the control of the associational life of the community by the influential group, without incumbency in political or otherwise constituted offices, had reached the point that personal eccentricities were becoming legend. In Southeast County, legend features failed to influence project decisions and did not deter a participant who tended ". . . to ramrod things through in spite of opposition." Again, an understanding of the decision-making process in Southeast County rested largely on a penetration of the structural setting; in Noreast, on an assessment of the social-psychological content of influence.

XIII. IN RETROSPECT

THE IDEA that health ought to be a community enterprise has come to fruition in widely separated points of the United States. So it was that this research set out to trace its growth within a certain type of community—that limited in population and resources. As demonstrations of community action, the research was focused on the distinguishing characteristics of community action within six regional areas of the United States.

Together, the research and this report constitute a detailed review of community action in small American communities. Throughout the study, the accent has been on the community and its resources for citizen-action, rather than on health itself, either environmentally or institutionally. As a comparative study, it threw into relief certain contrasts among the areas studied. Not only were the individual patterns of community action deemed important, but, likewise, the contrasts in patterns.

County Government: The Keynote

THE FINDINGS of the study stake out some guidelines for future planning toward major health goals in small communities. The first requisite is a recognition of the strategic position of county government. It is true that hospitals are normally constructed on town or city sites, but the most popular hospital jurisdictional unit, for the 218 Hill-Burton hospital projects, was the county. The consistent exception occurred in the projects of the Northeast Region. In most cases the constituted enabling authority for the decision-making process resided in the county governmental structure. At other times the county governing body provided only necessary approval for decisions made by extra-legal hospital procurement groups.

The strength of county governing bodies frequently determined how decision-making capacities were organized, the style of negotiation, and the form of sponsorship and administration of hospital building and maintenance. One distinctive contrast was found in the ways in which small town citizens cooperated in relation to respective county governing bodies. Sometimes the flow of citizen-action included the incumbents of county governing offices as important participants. At other times the flow of citizen-action failed to add an actively participating official from the county governing body. An explanation for this contrast is found in the internal organization of the governing body.

The Southeast regional grouping of hospital projects, as well as Southeast County itself, was characterized by county governing bodies with a hierarchical arrangement of officials. Certain offices of constituted authority were found to have a stronger position than others. Hence, the office of probate judge in Southeast County was superordinate to the other members of the Commissioners' Court. Official incumbents of such superior positions tended to take an active part in decision-making processes even when carried out apart from the county governing body. This participation facilitated transfer of community action to the county governmental structure, where it remained until successful completion of hospital construction. Whenever this occurred in the interests of effective project completion hierarchical relationships were commonly present within the county governing body.

When the incumbents of superordinate offices within the respective county governing body did play an active role in hospital construction, certain consequences tended to follow. Community efforts were accordingly more decisive as measured by success after but one campaign. A relatively fewer number of participants engaged actively in the project. There was increased use of legal instrumentalities to raise funds, and correspondingly less concern with communication and appeal to the community-at-large.

Hierarchical internal organization of the county governing body was not the rule. Notably exhibited in the Midstate, Farwest, and Norwest cases were county governing bodies with officials representing territorial subdivisions of the county but without evident arrangement of superordinate offices. Thus, no incumbent of a particular office was legally delegated the authority to control the process of hospital procurement.

In such instances—although community citizens were still commonly confronted with obtaining approval of the county government—the governing body participated as a total group. This participation was largely limited to formalizing approval of decisions made outside the structure of county government. The flow of community action, with its related decision-making processes, failed to lodge with county government. The major consequence here was that the community-at-large became directly and increasingly involved in decision-making processes. A more extensive community-wide organization resulted. With this type of action, the decisiveness of the pattern, as measured by success after but one campaign, was reduced. Particularly was this the case in Norwest county. However, less decisiveness in procuring the hospital may, in the future, be counter-balanced by a greater number of people supporting the institution when in operation.

This condensed review of majority characteristics does not, however, apply to the Northeast regional grouping of projects, nor specifically, to the Noreast case. For the Northeastern hospital projects, not a single county or municipal governing body was reported to be centrally important in sponsoring hospital construction. The substitutes were various agencies specializing in hospital procurement, construction, and maintenance.

These forms of initiation and sponsorship were usually followed by extensive organizational plans in the respective communities. Predominant among them was the fund-raising campaign in charge of the professional fund-raiser. Extensive organizational activities for fund-raising formed frequently about a small group of influential persons often sharing experience and reciprocal obligation in community affairs. Tangent to such organized voluntary plans, almost always, was a male service club. Notably absent were incumbents of local political offices. Characteristically present were fund-raising methods of a voluntary nature.

Because of this group of attributes, the Northeast cases, and some in other regions, cannot be keynoted entirely by an attention to county government. Municipal government is scarcely more relevant. Instead, the expediting clue becomes the associational structure of the community. While incumbents of local governing offices are absent, in their places are prominent workers in the community possessing public-accredited resources and proficiencies.

It is true, indeed, that the political unit of the county and the instrumentality of county government were consistent features of decision-making throughout the 218 hospital projects. The previous treatment does, however, indicate that there is a progressive trend away from reliance on these elements as the location of community health action moves clockwise from the Southeast and Southwest areas of the United States around to the urbanized Northeast, where a convergence of voluntary elements for community action occurs and more extensive organizational arrangements are present.

There are certain implications for community planning and action toward major health goals in the high incidence of county governments as centrally important groups in constructing hospitals and providing public health services. For major projects of the hospital type, citizen-effort depends for its effectiveness on an understanding of the structure of county government. This understanding would comprehend not only the interplay between county government and other influential segments of the given area, but also the internal organization of the presiding governing body, itself.

The frequent dissatisfaction of lay and professional workers at failure to obtain cooperation from local governing groups ought to result, in future projects, in more attention to the integration of goverment with the community action flow toward major health facilities than it has before. This need might be met in two ways. The first technique is the more extensive involvement of individual members of county governing groups in the early planning stages. This would replace strategies which premises the county governing body as some future target. The second method is the inclusion of governmental representatives in informal training programs so that they may keep pace with the need for an increase of hospital and public health services. Additional county governing officials might be added to adult education programs in which other citizen groups participate in order to expand their proficiencies (especially of subject-matter). Likewise, the provision for future training experiences should not overlook the hundreds of new health and hospital board members, who, for better or worse, will condition the administration of many health facilities.

Welfare or Business

ONE SHARP contrast was visible in the character of local efforts to obtain hospitals as compared to the campaigns for local health departments. A thread of comparison is suggested throughout the study of the respective efforts. The advent of a hospital in the community frequently encountered public interpretations of good business management. On the other hand, the creation of the public health department had to deal with public estimations of its relation to public welfare in community affairs. The presence of these divergent interpretations was noted in the developmental stages toward the two major goals. The question really is this: To what extent will such estimations condition the use and support of these facilities in the service areas which have provided them?

The hospital project commonly drew its leadership from the business and executive occupations of the concerned community. Men rather than women filled the positions of leadership. A full two-thirds of the 670 persons named most active in the 218 hospital projects were either self-employed businessmen, professional workers, or managers and executives. The hospital project was not predominantly the product of rural leaders nor of employed workers. Yet, in many of the 218 hospital communities of interest to this study, it will be the families of farmers and workers who will use the services of the new hospital most extensively.

On the other hand, the local health department sprang from different community roots than did the hospital. The leadership of men was not so pronounced. Business and executive facets of the community were not in the vanguard. Instead, housewives and professional workers formed councils and committees and, today, are accredited with developing the new services of local health departments. Two-thirds of the leadership for public health came from the ranks of professional workers and housewives.

The problems of hospital construction revolved about a central axis of money, sites, and blueprints. The questions raised were largely those of taxes, bonds, and building specifications. The primary concern of the public was commonly with the future ability of the hospital to be a self-sufficient service. There were actually few questions raised about the need for additional hospital facilities.

Many questions were raised, however, about the economic feasibility of the new hospital—not only the initial cost of construction, but the later management of need, occupancy, and hospital costs. As an informant in one case study declared, "I'll wager that the board members of the new hospital will send their families to the big city hospitals. They always have. The trouble will be that the people who can afford hospital service won't use our small one. That leaves us with the people who can't afford it anywhere. How the thing (the hospital) will break even in this way no one has bothered to figure out." Such anxieties traced to rather widespread interpretations of hospital economics, and not to uncertainties about the need for more adequate hospital facilities.

The problems of acquiring additional public health services pivoted about somewhat different axes. First of all, public skepticism about need for public health services was much more apparent than was true of the hospital developments. As reported by health officers of departments already organized and by other informants, questions of actual need were raised by the medical profession, local governing bodies, and specialized professional associations. Although the hospital projects reported in only 14 per cent of the instances that critics recommended another solution, the local health department projects encountered such recommendations in 37 percent of the cases. Informants reporting on their experiences in developing local health departments cautioned over and over again that the public could easily construe public health services as an extension of charity and welfare. One health officer emphasized, "—settle the rumors that the health department is something 'for free.' " With such interpretations set in motion in the community or county, perhaps it is not surprising to find county governing bodies reported as apathetic to public health services.

Brief comparisons such as these suggest that health services in the small town and rural areas of America relate to two clusters of values held by the people. One cluster has to do with business and good management. The other has to do with health as a problem of charity and welfare. These divergent estimations actually make the hospital and the local health department two different goals for community health action. Hence, differing occupational segments of the community assume leadership, and the anxieties of community development are rooted in differing value orientations.

These findings suggest, as the professional public health worker may be much aware, that the publics of small communities and rural areas have some distance to travel before public health services are seen in relation to the total health environment of the home community. The truth seems to be that acquiring a local health department calls for more and better education and community understanding in the initial stages than does acquiring a hospital. There is reason to speculate whether an increasing emphasis on the total configuration of community health services, including both hospital and public health, and the important functions which each may have for the other, might serve to counteract this separation of function in the public mind.

Too, there are elements of public policy at the local level which sometimes appear to confuse the issue. These may deal with the responsibilities of local government, the patterns of financing, the combination of governmental units into larger service areas, and the eventual coordination of health services (and not the least among them, hospital and public health services). Another hazard to community action for modern health facilities may be a widespread feeling that the job is done when the services are obtained. Awareness is growing that intelligent administration and use after the services are created is really a long second chapter in the story of community action toward providing services for healthful community living.

Office and Skill

REPEATED mention has been made throughout this report to the differential incidence in various projects of governing and other offices and the resources and proficiencies of influence. Also, the study analysis was preoccupied with the extent to which the region offers an opportunity to view sub-cultures in American society. The assumption was made that the complex of historical, cultural, and technological factors articulate in such a way as to express themselves in varying styles of community problem-solving.

The scientific problem begins only at this point—to isolate the factors of structure and process that are distinctly regional in nature. That the concept of region is applicable to the development of health facilities was borne out. Certain instrumentalities were found to be characteristic of regional localization, cooperative medicine in the Southwest and Northwest and hospital districts in the Far West. However, the use of the region in comparative research still remains an issue of debate which this study does not materially lessen.

This study suggests a need to isolate those factors that relate directly to community process and which appear variously in regional groupings of community projects. Among these would be the form and internal structure of county government in varied administrative units, the jurisdictional relationships of municipalities to the county (with attending interest in the changing function of the county in local problem-solving), and the very nature of jurisdictional authority, both county and municipal, in its diffuse and concentrated forms. The relation of special interest groups to various local administrative patterns should not be overlooked.

Throughout the present study the most meager analysis could not miss some differences. Such a one was the extent to which the decision-making process was focused here in municipalities and there in counties. The Southeast and Midstate cases were distinctly oriented to the county as the prime area for decision-making, although the latter revealed certain difficulties in reconciling the interests of municipalities with those of the county. In the Farwest case, there was accomplished an effective interplay between the county and municipalities, but with the latter as an informal focus of the decision-making process. In Norwest, the arena for decision-making was clearly behind the store fronts on Main Street of Norwestville. Finally, the jurisdiction of the county was completely by-passed in Noreast, as the business complex of the city successfully engineered a professionalized campaign to raise sufficient funds.

Such contrasting patterns of municipal-county linkage seem to have little importance when they stand alone. When the contrasts are placed alongside other coincidences, clearer regional patterns emerge. First among these is the observation that men of reputed skill enter the decision-making function when the municipality serves as the arena rather than the county. In such instances, the reins were in the hands of the lawyer, the legal consultant, the engineer, the oil company executive, and the professional fund-raiser—not probate judges, county supervisors, and circuit judges. In each of the Farwest, Norwest, and Noreast cases, strangers to local community and county affairs were called into the service of getting a new hospital. The criteria for calling them forth were those of skill, not of authority.

The second coincidence is that when men of skill carried out the decision-making function, with the municipality rather than the county serving as the arena of operation, the organization of the people-at-large was more extensive. Instead of a small group of office holders doing necessary work as in Southeast County, men and women organized and attended mass meetings, served on

161

and directed committees, planned and went to afternoon teas, campaign auctions, and testimonial banquets in the project's interest. Yet, not all local people possessed the skill of Noreast's professional fund-raiser. In the mass, such hospital projects, with all their gain in participation, lacked the decisiveness of those in which the incumbents of local governing offices were active participants.

These implications may suggest to researchers that in the details of decision-making and community problem-solving, the patterning of office and skill are not to be overlooked. Then, too, there is the broader question of the possible relationships with the impact of urbanization on small communities. Is the distinctiveness of the Northeast grouping of hospital projects and of the Noreast case, notwithstanding historical and cultural factors, related to the urbanization of small communities in the Northeast?

Methodologically, however, the notion of urbanization would be no more fruitful than that of region unless certain indices of urbanization could be determined and an array of communities selected accordingly. The uniformity of the communities employed in the present study offered little opportunity for ordering the cases according to this continuum. Further studies might alter the composition by, for instance, attention to rural-urban population balance and total population in the service areas. The research problem might well include the study of the influence (especially of proficiency) and authority differential in community action found in community sites placed progressively along an urbanization continuum.

Community workers giving on-the-ground assistance to community projects frequently assume that a given style of community action will be appropriate for solving most problems. The present study suggests that the nature of the problem makes a difference. Community organizational research may profitably become concerned with the suiting of the style of community action to the problem.

The present study indicates that even variation as to type of health goal produces the activation of varying occupational groups, alters the age and sex characteristics of participants, and calls forth different special interest groups.

To reconstruct the decision-making process in comparable communities, with the goal varied, should also more greatly define these clusters of values which lend "rightfulness" to the making of community decisions. Other community problems, lying outside the area of health, may evoke responses from groups and decision-makers of an altogether different order from that found in the present study. Such investigation would examine the extent to which there are distinctive social domains of decision-making within the field of community action. The order of problem or goal to which decision-making is directed may be a determinant in specifying which domains are activated.

With a View to Research

As IMPLIED before, this study indicates that channels of communication between municipal and county governmental units are often poorly developed. Further study is needed of the manner in which people bring before and negotiate their proposals with constituted governing groups at the local level. At this point, the importance of the male service club could scarcely be overlooked. The service club in small-town America serves as a chief vehicle in pyramiding and articulating influence within the total community. Likewise, the male service club is frequently the connecting link between the rural and urban components of the community, and between those accredited with needed proficiencies in community action and the incumbents in offices of authority.

The difficulties encountered in the present study should encourage interest in perfecting the methodological tools of performing both adequate and useful studies of community functioning. Although the reconstruction of events which produced new hospitals was the major approach, its future use could be perfected by the sharpening of interview methods, the improved selection of necessary informants, and the inclusion of those residents who did not participate in decision-making. These tasks should enable "event reconstruction" to make rapid process in community studies.

This major approach enables the selection of many communities for comparative work, lends to preliminary selection and study, rather than a precipitation into current and ongoing action plans by expedient and fortuitous circumstances. However, the "event reconstruction" approach runs the risk of confining the field workers to an unvarying circle of what is surmised to be relevancy to the particular project. Thus, the field worker may never fully ascertain the nature of the decision-making process because he has limited himself to paths of "relevancy" which may be only the paths of ready "visibility." Community action research ought to include more than the interpretations of the decision-makers themselves. Indeed, the consequences of the decisions must be learned from those to whom they apply.

A deficiency of the present study is its lack of concern with the totally unsuccessful cases of action toward major health goals. An important task still remains in employing the "event reconstruction" approach for comparative studies of both success and lack of success in reaching similar community goals. Undoubtedly, the present methods of devising plans for field study require ample alterations to make this practicable.

But with all this directed to the type of investigation attempted, there still remains the fact that the study deals with but one segment of the present movement in the United States to facilitate more adequate medical care. This segment is the behavior of small communities in obtaining the major goals of the hospital, the local health department, and the consumer-sponsored prepayment plan.

The hospital procurement efforts of this recent period have been, for small-town America, community projects of almost unprecedented magnitude. Yet, the provision of the facilities is but one chapter of the total story. The other chapters will be told in the adjustments of small communities to the new facility, the interplay of institutions and community, and the effectiveness of public relations and human relations in adjusting a new service to the needs of the community.

The way in which the story will eventuate offers a rich opportunity for research and assistance to community action. In this important field there is as yet no analysis of the continuing reverberations that course through communities across the breadth of the nation when they initiate, secure, and utilize a major medical facility.

BIBLIOGRAPHICAL APPENDIX

A NOTE ON METHOD

1. Because of this legislation specifically allocating federal funds to assist with the construction costs of local hospitals meeting certain required standards, the number of such projects would weigh heavily in any inventory of recent small-town hospital developments. This being the case, it seemed best to limit this particular treatment to Hill-Burton hospitals entirely, providing an additional basis of comparability. For the details of the legislative program to provide partial assistance (originally one-third of the total cost) to local hospital projects, see Congress of the United States, "Hospital Survey and Construction Act, Public Law 725," *United States Statutes At Large*, Vol. 60, Part I, pp. 1040–1049, U. S. Govt. Printing Office, Washington, D. C.

2. Cf. Federal Security Agency, *National Hospital Program, Status Report, Nov. 30, 1949,* Hospital Facilities Division, U. S. Public Health Service, Washington, D. C., 1949.

3. H. W. Odum, *Southern Regions of the United States,* University of North Carolina Press, Chapel Hill, 1936; also, H. W. Odum and H. E. Moore, *American Regionalism,* Henry Holt and Co., New York, 1938.

Other studies of regionalism that were reviewed are: C. C. Taylor, *et al.,* from A. F. Raper, "Rural Social Differentials" (Ch. 18), *Rural Life in the United States,* Alfred H. Knopf, New York, 1949, p. 309; C. P. Loomis and J. A. Beegle, *Rural Social Systems,* Prentice-Hall, Inc. New York, 1950, pp. 249–250; P. G. Beck and M. C. Forster, *Six Rural Problem Areas,* Research Monograph I, Federal Emergency Relief Administration, Washington, D. C., 1935; A. R. Mangus, *Rural Regions of the United States,* Work Projects Administration, Washington, D. C., 1940; see also for the development of sub-areas in Ohio, C. E. Lively and R. B. Almack, *A Method of Determining Rural Social Sub-Areas With Application to Ohio,* Ohio AES Mimeograph Bulletin No. 106, January, 1938. For some critical comments on the concept of region as employed by sociologists, see O. D. Duncan and E. F. Sharp, "Rural Sociological Research in the Wheat Belt," *Rural Sociology,* Vol. 15, 1950, No. 4, pp. 339–340 and p. 351; L. Wirth, "Limitations of Regionalism," in M. Jensen, *Regionalism in America,* The University of Wisconsin Press, Madison, 1951, p. 392: "The failure to discriminate the many distinct factors that underlie the emergence and persistence of regions is a serious fault of present-day scholarship and research. It has led to the failure to distinguish between genuine and spurious regions. Areas of homogeneity have been mistakenly represented as areas of integration. It has been mistakenly assumed that physical regions also inevitably constitute economic, cultural, and political regions. . . . As a tool for the discernment of interrelations between habitat and culture the regional concept has great value, provided we do not assume what needs to be proved, namely, that these correlations actually exist, and proceed to analyze the processes that account for these correlations."

For studies referring to regional developments in health: F. D. Mott and M. I. Roemer, *Rural Health and Medical Care,* McGraw-Hill, New York, 1948, pp. 554-5; see also the following reports on regional health developments: Northern Great Plains Council, Subcommittee on Health, *Medical Care and Health Services for Farm Families of the Northern Great Plains*, Lincoln, Neb., 1945; L. B. Tate (ed.), "The South's Health: A Picture with Promise," Hearings before the Special Subcommittee on Cotton of the Committee on Agriculture, House of Representatives, 80th Cong., 1st Sess., *Study of Agricultural and Economic Problems of the Cotton Belt*, Govt. Printing Office, 1947, pp. 808-76. A variety of regional references are made in University of Michigan, School of Public Health, *Public Health Economics: A Monthly Compilation of Events and Opinions*, especially the issues of 1945, 1946, and 1947; see also *Regional Planning and Development*, University of North Carolina, Chapel Hill, January, 1951.

4. H. L. Johnston, *Rural Health Cooperatives*, FCA Bulletin 60, PHS Bulletin 308, Washington, D. C., 1950; J. Warbasse, *Cooperative Medicine*, 4th edition, Cooperative League of the U. S. A., 1946, Farm Credit Administration, "Cooperative Health Articles," reprinted from the *News for Farmer Cooperatives*, Series I, revised June, 1947, Washington, D. C.; M. C. Klem, *Prepayment Medical Care Organizations*, Social Security Board, Bureau of Research and Statistics, Memo. 55, Federal Security Agency, June, 1945; N. Sinai, O. W. Anderson, and M. L. Dollar, *Health Insurance in the United States*, The Commonwealth Fund, New York, 1946; also, the unpublished studies of W. C. Rohrer, formerly of Texas Agricultural and Mechanical College, College Station, and E. L. Robinson, Texas State College for Women, Denton.

I. PERSPECTIVE

1. See, for example, A. R. Mangus and J. R. Seeley, *Mental Health Needs in a Rural and Semi-Rural Area of Ohio*, Mimeo. Bulletin No. 195, Ohio State University, Columbus, January, 1947; also, A. R. Mangus, "Personality Adjustment of Rural and Urban Children," *American Sociological Review*, Vol. 13, October, 1948, pp. 566-575.

2. C. R. Hoffer, *et al.*, *Health Needs and Health Care in Michigan*, AES Bulletin 365, Michigan State College, East Lansing, June, 1950; C. R. Hoffer and E. A. Schuler, "Determination of Unmet Need for Medical Care Among Michigan Farm Families," *Journal of the Michigan State Medical Society*, Vol. 46, April, 1947, pp. 443-446.

3. For example, see C. E. Lively and P. G. Beck, *The Rural Health Facilities of Ross County, Ohio*, AES Bulletin 412, Ohio State University, Columbus, October, 1927; R. B. Almack, *The Rural Health Facilities of Lewis County, Missouri*, AES Bulletin 365, University of Missouri, Columbia, 1943.

4. H. L. Hitt and A. L. Bertrand, *The Social Aspects of Hospital Planning*, Louisiana Study Series No. 1, Health and Hospital Division, Office of the Governor, Baton Rouge, August, 1947; *Hospital Resources and Needs*, The Report of the Michigan Hospital Survey, W. K. Kellogg Foundation, Battle Creek, 1946.

5. H. F. Dorn, *Maternal Mortality in Rural and Urban Areas*, Public Health Reports, Vol. 54, April 28, 1939; P. M. Houser, *Mortality Differentials in Michigan*, unpublished Ph.D. dissertation, Michigan State College, East Lansing, 1948.

6. O. W. Anderson, "Compulsory Medical Care Insurance, 1910-1950," *The Annals of the American Academy of Political and Social Science*, January, 1951; B. J. Stern, *Social Factors in Medical Progress*, Columbia University Press, New York, 1927.

7. See, for example, the following: "The Fortune Survey," *Fortune*, Vol. 26, July, 1942; National Opinion Research Center, "Social Security," *Public Opinion*

Quarterly, Vol. 7, 1943; C. F. Reuse, *Farmer Views on the Medical Situation*, AES Bulletin (V. Circ.) 20, State College of Washington, Pullman, 1944; R. W. Roskelley, *The Rural Citizen and Medical Care*, AES Bulletin 495, State College of Washington, Pullman, 1947.

8. T. Parsons, *The Social System*, The Free Press, Glencoe, Illinois, 1951, (Ch. X: "Social Structure and Dynamic Process: The Case of Modern Medical Practice"), pp. 428–473; O. Hall, "The Stages of a Medical Career," *American Journal of Sociology*, Vol. 53, 1948, pp. 327–336; O. Garceau, *The Political Life of the American Medical Association*, Harvard University Press, Cambridge, 1941; O. Hall, "Types of Medical Careers," *American Journal of Sociology*, Vol. 55, 1949, pp. 243–253; A. Joseph, "Physician and Patient," *Applied Anthropology*, Vol. 1, 1942, pp. 1–17.

9. Acknowledgments are due the influence of the following for an orientation to the idea of community; R. M. MacIver, *Society: A Textbook of Society*, Farrar and Rinehart, New York, 1937, p. 284; C. C. Taylor, "Techniques of Community Study and Analysis as Applied to Modern Civilized Societies," in R. Linton (ed.), *The Science of Man in the World Crisis*, Columbia University Press, New York, 1945, pp. 435–436.

See also L. A. Cook, "Meaning of Community," *Educational Method*, Vol. 18, 1939, pp. 259–262, for a useful definition of community; also E. T. Hiller, "The Community as a Social Group," *American Sociological Review*, Vol. 6, 1941, pp. 189–202, for a summary of various definitions of community.

10. See O. R. Ewing, *The Nation's Health: A Ten Year Program*, Federal Security Agency, Washington, D. C., 1948.

11. R. S. Lynd and H. M. Lynd, *Middletown: A Study in Contemporary American Culture*, Harcourt, Brace and Co., New York, 1929; *Middletown in Transition: A Study in Cultural Conflicts*, Harcourt, Brace and Co., New York, 1937. J. West, *Plainville*, Columbia University Press, New York, 1945; R. Redfield, *The Folk Culture of Yucatan*, University of Chicago Press, Chicago, 1941; M. Yang, *The Chinese Village*, Columbia University Press, New York, 1945.

12. See, for example, the first in the series: W. W. Warner and P. S. Lunt, *The Social Life of a Modern Community*, Yale University Press, New Haven, 1941.

13. H. Powdermaker, *After Freedom: A Cultural Study in the Deep South*, The Viking Press, New York, 1939; A. Davis and B. B. and M. R. Gardner, *Deep South: A Social Anthropological Study of Caste and Class*, University of Chicago Press, Chicago, 1941; S. C. Drake and H. R. Cayton, *Black Metropolis*, Harcourt, Brace and Co., New York, 1945; and J. Dollard, *Caste and Class in a Southern Town*, Yale University Press, New Haven, 1947.

14. O. Leonard and C. P. Loomis, *El Cerrito, New Mexico*, No. 1, 1941; E. H. Bell, *Sublette, Kansas*, No. 2, 1942; K. MacLeish and K. Young, *Landoff, New Hampshire*, No. 3, 1942; W. M. Kollmorgan, *The Old Amish of Lancaster County, Pennsylvania*, No. 4, 1942; E. O. Moe and C. C. Taylor, *Irwin, Iowa*, No. 5, 1942; W. Wynne, *Harmony, Georgia*, No. 6, 1943. See also C. C. Taylor, "Techniques of Community Study and Analyses Applied to Modern Civilized Societies," *The Science of Man in the World Crisis*, Columbia University Press, 1945, pp. 419–424; for a critical appraisal of these and other studies, see A. B. Hollingshead, "Community Research: Development and Present Condition," *American Sociological Review*, 1948, Vol. 13, pp. 139–140.

15. Jess and Jean Ogden, *These Things We Tried*, University of Virginia Extension, Charlottesville, 1947; Jess and Jean Ogden, *Small Communities in Action*, Harper and Bros., New York, 1946; I. T. Sanders (ed.), *Making Good Communities Better*, University of Kentucky Press, Lexington, 1950; A. Hillman, *Com-*

munity Organization and Planning, The Macmillan Co., New York, 1950; see, also, W. J. Hayes, *The Small Community Looks Ahead*, Harcourt, Brace and Co., New York, 1947; A. E. Morgan, *The Small Community*, Harper and Bros., New York, 1942.

16. J. H. Steward, *Area Research: Theory and Practice*, Social Science Research Council, New York, Bulletin 63, 1950. Recognition, either for purposes of sampling within larger areas or ascertaining the interplay between individual communities and larger sociocultural areas, is given in the following: C. M. Arensberg and S. T. Kimball, *Family and Community in Ireland*, Harvard University Press, Cambridge, 1940; recent Peruvian studies in the Andean highlands; and in regional studies in Puerto Rico (J. H. Steward, *op. cit.*, pp. 133–139).

17. Reference may be made to the classic concept of "definition of the situation," generally accredited to W. I. Thomas. See E. H. Volkart, *Social Behavior and Personality*, Social Science Research Council, New York, 1951, pp. 1–32, 57–58, 80–81, and 170–175; see also other interpretations: R. E. Park and E. E. Burgess, *Introduction to the Science of Sociology*, Univ. of Chicago Press, Chicago, 1921, p. 764.

18. J. Bryce, *The Modern Democracies*, (Ch. 75, "Oligarchies Within Democracies"), Vol. 2, The Macmillan Co., New York, 1924, p. 542; R. M. MacIver, *The Web of Government*, The Macmillan Co., New York, 1947, pp. 83–84.

19. H. D. Lasswell and A. Kaplan, *Power and Society*, Yale University Press, New Haven, 1950, p. 74; H. D. Lasswell, *An Analysis of Political Behavior*, Oxford University Press, New York, 1947, pp. 37–38; R. M. MacIver, *op. cit.*, p. 9; R. Bierstedt, "An Analysis of Social Power," *American Sociological Review*, Vol. 15, 1950, p. 733.

20. MacIver, *op. cit.*, p. 225; M. J. Hillenbrand, *Power and Morals*, Columbia University Press, New York, 1949, pp. 134–191; G. Ferrero, *The Principles of Power*, New York, 1942, p. 135.

21. H. D. Lasswell and A. Kaplan, *op. cit.*, pp. 74–75; R. K. Merton, *Social Theory and Social Structure*, The Free Press, Glencoe, Ill., 1949, p. 67: "In short, it is suggested that the *distinctive* intellectual contributions of the sociologist are found primarily in the study of unintended consequences (among which are latent functions) of a given practice, as well as in the study of anticipated consequences (among which are manifest functions)." For such studies see A. K. Davis, "Bureaucratic Patterns in Navy Officer Corps," *Social Forces*, Vol. 27, 1948, pp. 143–153; F. J. Roethlisberger and W. J. Dickson, *Management and the Worker*, Harvard University Press, Cambridge, 1939; P. Selznick, *TVA and the Grass Roots*, Univ. of California Press, Berkeley, 1949; and basic is the classic concept of "conspicuous consumption" by T. Veblen, *The Theory of the Leisure Class*, Vanguard Press, New York, 1928.

22. R. M. MacIver, *The Web of Government*, The Macmillan Co., New York, 1947, p. 83; H. D. Lasswell and A. Kaplan, *op. cit.*, p. 133.

23. E. T. Hiller, *Social Relations and Structures*, Harper and Bros., New York, 1947, pp. 582–583. For a statement of difference between social power, authority, and dominance, see R. Bierstedt, *op. cit.*, pp. 732–733, i. e., "Power is a sociological, dominance a psychological, concept. . . . The locus of power is in groups and it expresses itself in interpersonal relations. Power appears in the statuses which people occupy in formal organization; dominance in the roles they play in informal organization." (p. 732); K. Davis, *Human Society*, The Macmillan Co., New York, 1949, pp. 88–98.

24. W. W. Warner and R. Lunt, *op. cit.*, passim.

25. H. D. Lasswell and A. Kaplan, *op. cit.*, p. 55.

26. H. D. Lasswell, *Power and Personality*, W. W. Norton and Co., New York, 1948, p. 17; see also W. W. Warner and P. Lunt, *The Social Life of a Modern Community*, Yale Univ. Press, New Haven, 1941, p. 125.

27. H. D. Lasswell speaks of "rectitude," "uprightness," and "moral standing" as components of many political careers based on moral integrity. See his *Power and Personality*, W. W. Norton and Co., New York, 1948, pp. 29-30. L. D. Zeleny speaks of "moral ascendency" as a component of influence for the leader, in "Morale and Leadership," *Journal of Applied Sociology*, Vol. 9, 1925, p. 210; and E. T. Hiller declares: ". . . honor . . . measuring up to the best standards of technical competence and fair dealings (such as equity in utilitarian transactions), but also as a recognition of the importance or worth of the part one plays in society." *op. cit.*, p. 492.

28. *Ibid.*

29. Cf. F. S. Chapin, "Leadership and Group Activity," *Journal of Applied Sociology*, Vol. 8, 1924, pp. 141-145, for findings regarding the overlapping participation of leaders in various groups in the community. This author suggests the hypothesis: "Polarization of leadership within the community as between groups tends to elaborate until some leader's range of elasticity for participation in group activity is passed, when some one or more groups begin to disintegrate until an equilibrium of group activity is restored." (p. 145)

30. See T. F. Neely, "The Sources of Political Power: A Contribution to the Sociology of Leadership," *American Journal of Sociology*, Vol. 33, 1928, p. 769: "Despite the corruption in machine politics, the methods used by the boss in gaining power are based on sound sociopsychological principles, because most bosses rule by the consent of the people. The essential factor in boss control is an appeal to the personal loyalty and friendship of individuals made through the philanthropic work and social life of the machine and the personal contacts of the boss"; see also R. K. Merton, *Social Theory and Social Structure*, The Free Press, Glencoe, Ill., 1949, pp. 73-81; also H. F. Harold Gosnell, *Machine Politics*, The Univ. of Chicago Press, Chicago, 1938; E. J. Flynn, "Bosses and Machines," *The Atlantic*, May, 1947, pp. 34-40.

31. See H. D. Lasswell, "Policy and the Intelligence Function," in *The Analysis of Political Behavior*, Oxford University Press, New York, 1947, p. 127: "Policy thinking . . . is always guided to some extent by knowledge; and a recurring problem is to perfect the intelligence function so that it brings to the focus of attention of the decision-maker what he most needs to think about and what he most needs to think with." See H. D. Lasswell and A. Kaplan, *op. cit.*, p. 55, for "enlightenment"; also, E. D. Sanderson, *Leadership for Rural Life*, Association Press, New York, 1940, for the leader as "group educator," (p. 33); L. D. Zeleny, "Leadership," *Encyclopedia of Education Research*, (Paul Munroe, ed.), 1941, p. 665.

32. See C. E. Merriam, in "Political Power," *A Study of Power*, The Free Press, Glencoe, Ill., 1950, for a reference to "facility in group combination," p. 41. See also P. Pigors, *Leadership and Domination*, Houghton Mifflin Co., New York, 1935, in reference to "administration as a function of leadership," pp. 248-252; H. M. Busch, *Leadership in Group Work*, Association Press, New York, 1934: "In working with the natural or gang group the leader's task is . . . to recruit . . . special abilities . . . to secure . . . new members . . . to relate his group . . . to wider programs." (p. 230); also, H. D. Lasswell, *The Analysis of Political Behavior*, Oxford University Press, New York, 1947, p 102, for a discussion of "skills in management" (from the vantage point of the decision-maker).

33. See W. Lippman, "Leaders and the Rank and File," in *Public Opinion*, The Macmillan Co., New York, 1922: ". . . the symbol is both a mechanism of solidarity

and a mechanism of exploitation. It enables people to work for a common end, but just because the few who are strategically placed must choose the concrete objectives, the symbol is also an instrument by which a few can fatten on many, deflect criticism, and seduce men into facing agony for objects they do not understand." (p. 236); "And so where masses of people must cooperate in an uncertain and eruptive environment, it is usually necessary to secure unity and flexibility without real consent. The symbol does that. It obscures personal intention, neutralizes discrimination, and obfuscates individual purpose. It immobilizes personality, yet at the same time it enormously sharpens the intention of the group and welds the group, as nothing else in a crisis can weld it, to purposeful action." (p. 239)

See also H. D. Lasswell and A. Kaplan, *op. cit.*, for the comment: "Political symbols . . . constitutions, charters, laws, treaties, . . . party platforms, polemics, and slogans; speeches, editorials, forums on controversial subjects; political theories and philosophies . . . memorial days and periods; public places and monumental apparatus; music and songs; artistic designs in flags, decorations, statuary, uniforms; story and history; ceremonials of an elaborate nature, mass demonstrations with parades, oratory, music." (p. 103) Cf. C. E. Merriam, *Political Power*, McGraw-Hill, New York, 1934, 104 ff.; see also H. D. Lasswell, *The Analysis of Political Behavior*, Oxford Univ. Press, New York, 1947, pp. 123–124: "Each public policy calls for two types of intelligence: ideological and technical. By ideological intelligence is meant facts about the thoughts, feelings, and conduct of human beings. Other facts are technical. It makes no difference whether the policy goal is phrased in ideological or technical terms; both kinds of information are involved in any complete consideration of goals or alternatives."

34. Much of the literature on leadership, *per se*, assumes distinctive attributes of the leader, especially the "informal" leader. See, for example, R. M. Stogdill, "Personal Factors Associated with Leadership, A Survey of the Literature," *Journal of Psychology*, Vol. 25, pp. 37–71; G. W. Allport, "A Test for Ascendance-Submission," *Journal of Abnormal and Social Psychology*, Vol. 23, pp. 118–136; G. Murphy and L. B. Murphy, *Experimental Social Psychology*, Harper and Bros., New York, 1931, p. 404; W. F. Cowley, *op. cit.*, pp. 144–157; L. D. Zeleny, "Leadership," *Encyclopedia of Educational Research*, 1941, who speaks of "vitality"; P. F. Lazarsfeld, B. Berelson, H. Gaudet, "Informal Opinion Leaders and a National Election," in A. W. Gouldner, *Studies in Leadership*, Harper and Bros., New York, 1950, who speak of "political alertness."

See also L. D. Zeleny, "Characteristics of Group Leaders," *Sociology and Social Research*, Vol. 24, pp. 140–149, "vitality," "humility," "humor," and "voice quality"; see also L. A. Dexter, "Some Strategic Considerations in Innovating Leadership," in A. W. Gouldner, *op. cit.*, pp. 592–600.

II. BEDS, BRICKS, AND PEOPLE

1. See the following which stress the importance of value attitudes in local action settings: M. L. Wilson, *Cultural Approach to Extension Work*, Extension Circular 332, Washington, May, 1940; see also, American Association of Social Workers, *Community Organization, Its Nature and Setting*, Community Chests and Councils, Inc., New York. For the dynamic phase of community action as the recognition of "felt needs," see E. D. Sanderson and R. A. Polson, *Rural Community Organization*, John Wiley and Sons, New York, 1939; and C. M. King, *Organizing for Community Action*, Harper and Bros., New York, 1948.

2. Health education is an important and growing field of endeavor, as evidenced by a great variety of agencies and programs. See W. G. Smillie, *Public Health*

Administration in the United States, The Macmillan Co., New York, 1947; W. W. Bauer and T. G. Hull, *Health Education and the Public,* W. B. Saunders, New York, 2nd Edition, 1942.

For some of the devices employed in community health education, see I. A. Hiscock, *Ways to Community Health Education,* The Commonwealth Fund, Oxford Univ. Press, New York, 1939; M. Rugen, "Working Together for Better Health Education," *Journal of Educational Sociology,* Vol. 22, pp. 51-59; A. Oppenheim, "Health Education in Action," *American Journal of Public Health,* Vol. 33, 1943; B. G. Harvey, et al., "The Community Health Education Program," *American Journal of Public Health,* Vol. 31, pp. 310-318; C. E. Turner, *Community Organization for Health Education,* The Technology Press, 1941; also developing is the emphasis on rural health extension work in sixteen Land Grant Colleges, within the respective Cooperative Agricultural Extension Service; and see E. L. Anderson, *The Extension Service's Responsibility in Aiding Rural People to Improve Their Health and Medical Services, Extension Service Bulletin,* Washington, D. C., 1947.

3. See E. T. Hiller, *op. cit.,* p. 479: "Next to age and sex, occupation appears to be the most general basis on which rights and duties are assigned; for although no one escapes classification by age and sex, not everyone is assigned a vocational status." See also, D. C. Miller and W. H. Form, *Industrial Sociology,* Harper and Bros., New York, 1951, pp. 120-121; and W. W. Warner and P. S. Lunt, *op. cit.,* p. 261; J. H. Locke, *The Participation of Occupational Groups in Local Efforts to Obtain Hospital Services,* unpublished M. A. Thesis, Michigan State College, East Lansing, 1951.

4. The evidence suggests that the health council, beyond its defined function of coordination, has been related to public health programs within the community rather than hospital developments. A report by the National Health Council on selected characteristics of local health councils indicates that community needs frequently related to the functions of the health department resulted in the organization of a health council, as for example: "need to publicize work of Health Department," "need for sponsoring health project," "need for public health education," "to work for the establishment of a health department," "need to expand and improve Health Department." References are made to highly specific projects, i.e., "need to improve school health program." For this see *National Health Council Study of Health Councils,* mimeo., National Health Council, New York, October 30, 1950.

5. One author states: "From the experience of our survey (on libraries), the influence of the service clubs in cities under 200,000 population would seem to be greater than has been generally recognized." (O. Garceau, *The Public Library in the Political Process,* Columbia University Press, New York, 1949, p. 114.)

6. See C. M. King, *Organizing for Community Action,* Harper and Bros., New York, 1948, Chap. IV, which considers such questions as: "When may it be good technique to add an outsider to the committee to make it jell? . . . When is it helpful to have an objector on the committee?" In I. T. Sanders, *Making Good Communities Better,* Univ. of Kentucky Press, Lexington, 1950, will be found these statements: "The farther removed the planners are from the communities where the program is to be put into action, the less effective will be their planning. Programs too hastily devised and based on too limited observations of a few people frequently have to be changed later on; each unexpected change means added confusion and a loss of support for the program. Proper anticipation avoids later amputation." (p. 43); "A word of warning needs repeating; if the desire of a worker to set up a new organization . . . makes him ignore the existence of a well-

established group already associated in the public mind with the kind of a job to be done, by-passing it purposely may prove a serious blunder as well as a waste of available social resources." (p. 48); although concerned with the larger urban community, cf. the article by W. H. Form, "Mobilizing Urban Community Resources," in I. T. Sanders, *ibid.*, pp. 133-139. For example: "The larger the city grows the greater is the need for its sub-areas to cooperate in attaining common services and goals. Since size itself makes personal and spontaneous cooperation on a continuous basis almost impossible, special associations are created to meet special needs. Thus, in a real sense, organizations and institutions, not personalities, run the life of the city: . . . . "The first job of urban action-minded people, then, is to decide: (1) whether their problems are city-wide or local in character; (2) what organizations already exist on a city-wide or local basis." (p. 133)

7. For the details on the special hospital district, see *Laws Relating to Hospital Districts, An Excerpt from the California Health and Safety Code*, San Francisco, Department of Public Health, 1950 (Division 23: Hospital Districts, added by Statutes, 1945, ch. 932). Cf. par. 32001: "A local hospital may be organized, incorporated, and managed as provided in this division and may exercise the powers herein granted or necessarily implied. Such a district may include incorporated or unincorporated territory, or both, or territory in any one or more counties. The territory comprising this district need not be contiguous but the territory of a municipal corporation shall not be divided."

III. PREVENTING AND PAYING

1. For the legislative aspects of securing local health departments, especially his eight principles in such legislation, see Haven Emerson, *Local Health Units for the Nation*, The Commonwealth Fund, New York, 1945, pp. 329-330; also Haven Emerson, "Local Health Units for the Nation," *American Journal of Public Health*, Vol. 37, No. 1, Supplement, pp. 1-158.

2. For prepayment plan legislation, see O. W. Anderson, *State Enabling Legislation for Non-Profit Hospital and Medical Plans* (School of Public Health, Public Health Economic Research Series, No. 1), University of Michigan, Ann Arbor, 1944; James Warbasse, *Cooperative Medicine*, Cooperative League of the U. S. A., Chicago; M. C. Klem, *Recent State Legislation Concerning Prepayment Medical Care*, reprinted from Social Security Bulletin, Federal Security Agency, Social Security Administration, Washington, D. C., Jan., 1947; H. R. Hansen, *Laws Affecting Group Health Plans*, reprinted from the Iowa Law Review, Vol. 35, No. 2, Iowa City, Iowa, 1950, pp. 222-228; for the state-by-state development of permissive legislation as it pertains to rural cooperative associations, see E. G. Nourse, *The Legal Status of Agricultural Cooperation*, The Macmillan Company, New York, 1927. Since 52 of the 101 chartered cooperative prepayment plans have been in Texas (Johnston, *Rural Health Cooperatives*, FCA Bulletin 60, p. 5), some interest may be held in the specific legislative base of the Texas development: *Vernon's Civil Statutes of the State of Texas*, annotated, Article 1302, Sec. 2A (Acts of 1945, 49th Legislature, ch. 70, p. 102).

3. The health council is a specific form of the traditional community-wide citizens council, intended to serve primarily for the coordination of public and private health agencies in arriving at action programs in health. For definitions and the details of organization, see the American Medical Association, *The Community Health Council*, Council on Medical Service and Committee on Rural Health, 1949; American Public Health Association, "The Health Council and Its Possibilities," *American Journal of Public Health*, Vol. 33, pp. 757-759, July, 1944; J. W. Ferree,

"Health Councils and Their Potentialities," *Public Health Nursing*, Vol. 40, pp. 461–463, September, 1948; W. S. Groom, "What It Is and How It Works," *Journal of Health and Physical Education*, Vol. 17, pp. 332–334, June, 1946; S. S. Lifson, "The Role of the Community Health Council," *Public Health News*, July, 1948; Y. Lyon, *Stepping Stones to a Health Council*, National Health Council, New York, 1947; W. W. McFarland, "The Health Council, a Community Asset," *Hygeia*, Vol. 22, pp. 670–671, September, 1944; and M. Bleecker, "Health Councils in Local Communities," *American Journal of Public Health*, Vol. 37, pp. 959–966, August, 1947.

4. Health councils are not entirely a rural and small town device. A similar function is played by the Community Chest and the Council of Social Agencies in larger urban centers. An account of the Cincinnati Public Health Federation is revealing, in S. Gunn and P. Platt, *Voluntary Health Agencies*, The Roland Press, New York, 1945. For the details of organization and operation of the larger council, see the following: Coordinating Councils, Inc., *A Guide to Community Coordination*, Los Angeles, California, 1941; National Municipal League, *Citizens Councils*, New York, 1939; E. H. Kuser, "Community Councils: The Key to Making Democracy Work," *The Journal of Educational Sociology*, Vol. 20, pp. 201–203, December, 1946; M. G. Ross, *Community Councils*, Canadian Council of Education for Citizenship, Ottawa, February, 1945; S. D. Alinsky, "Community Analysis and Organization," *American Journal of Sociology*, Vol. 46, pp. 797–808, May, 1941; A. Dunham, *Community Councils in Action*, Community Organization Service, Philadelphia, 1929; A. F. Zander, "The Community Council," *Journal of Educational Sociology*, Vol. 13, pp. 525–532, May, 1940.

5. M. A. Shadid, *A Doctor for the People*, The Vanguard Press, New York, 1939.

6. See, for example, the manner in which a cooperative hospital and prepayment plan was developed in Amherst, Texas, in Farm Credit Administration, "Cooperative Health Articles," reprinted from the *News for Farmer Cooperatives*, U. S. Department of Agriculture, Washington, D. C., Series I, revised, June, 1947; see also H. L. Johnston, *Cooperation for Rural Health*, Cooperative Research Service Division, Farm Credit Administration, U. S. Department of Agriculture, Washington, D. C., September, 1948.

IV. REGION AND PROCESS

1. C. P. Loomis and J. Allan Beegle, *Rural Social Systems*, Prentice-Hall, New York, 1950, p. 304.

V. SOUTHEAST

1. See *Soils Areas of Alabama*, The Alabama Department of Agriculture and Industry, Montgomery, and Agricultural Experiment Station, Alabama Polytechnic Institute, Auburn, 1951.

2. This explanation did not altogether check with the field observers' impressions of the over-all social system, with which one author, at least, agrees. See, for example, V. O. Key, Jr., *Southern Politics*, A. A. Knopf, New York, 1949: "The planter may often be kind, even benevolent, towards his Negroes, and the up-countryman may be, as the Negroes say, 'mean'; yet, when the chips are down, the whites of the black belts by their voting demonstrate that they are most ardent in the faith of white supremacy as, indeed, would naturally be expected. The whites of the regions with few Negroes have a less direct concern over the maintenance

of white rule, whereas the whites of the black belts operate on economic and social system based on subordinate, black labor." (p. 9)

3. *Ibid.*, ". . . yet if the politics of the South revolves around any single theme, it is that of the role of the black belts. Although the whites of the black belts are few in number, their unity and their political skill have enabled them to run a shoestring into decisive power at critical junctures in southern political history." (p. 6)

4. *Ibid.*, "The chief figure in the governments of about two-thirds of the counties of Alabama is the probate judge. . . . The probate judge generally is the leader of the dominant faction within the county and often becomes the patriarch of the county. In many counties the potency of the probate judge demonstrates itself by a long string of re-elections." (p. 53)

5. *Ibid.*, "Factional machinery is generally of two broad kinds: first, that created for other purposes which is converted to campaigning purposes . . .; second, the essentially personal organization built up by each candidate among his acquaintances, admirers, and followers." (p. 53)

See K. A. Bosworth, *op. cit.*, "Personal following and factions . . . are significant factors in determining elections. . . . Also significant, at least for the probate judge . . . are the alignments which in some sense correspond to class lines; greatest strength in the towns, in the traditionally upper class black belt, in the more prosperous agricultural areas of the county, including the values of the hill section; least strength in the hill country and in areas of high white tenancy." (p. 16)

6. V. O. Key, Jr., *op. cit.*, "Probate judges are the ambassadors of their counties in dealing with the government and state departments." (p. 54)

7. See K. A. Bosworth, *op. cit.*, "Significant also is the fact that the judge identifies himself and is identified by others as a black belt politician. In a hill beat in which the judge had hoped to show strength because of the construction of a bridge there, he got only 4 out of the 58 votes. A day-before-election rumor had been passed about that the judge had said that he was a black belter, that the people of the hills weren't his kind, and that he didn't want their votes. The notions of class distinction die hard, especially where the horizon is short." (p. 16)

TABULAR APPENDIX

TABLE 1

REGIONAL LOCATION OF HOSPITAL PROJECTS IN ORIGINAL
AND RESPONDING INVENTORIES

	Original Inventory		Reporting Projects		Per Cent Reporting
Region	No.	Per Cent *	No.	Per Cent	Per Cent
Southeast	123	33	52	24	42
Southwest	50	13	25	12	50
Northeast	31	8	24	11	77
Middle States	76	20	58	26	76
Northwest	64	18	40	18	63
Far West	30	8	18	8	60
Unknown			1	1	
Total	374	100	218	100	58

* Percentage figures will be henceforth rounded off to whole numbers.

TABLE 2

OCCUPATIONAL POSITION OF PERSONS NAMED
MOST ACTIVE IN HOSPITAL PROJECTS

	Hospital Projects		Employed Workers* Male Labor Force
Occupation	Number	Percent	Percent
Self employed businessman	231	34	7**
Professional	180	28	5
Employed manager	107	16	4***
Farm owner or operator	69	10	14
Civil official	56	8	0****
Non-supervisory employee	27	4	57*****
Total	670	100	87******

* Estimated from the following: "Percent Distribution, by Social-Economic Groups, of Employed Workers (Except on Public Emergency Work), By Sex, for Division and States, 1940 (Table XXXI)," *Comparative Occupation Statistics for the United States,* 1870 to 1940, Sixteenth Census of the United States, 1940, p. 194. The computation of Employed Workers in the male labor force is, of course, not strictly comparable to the computation for the 218

reporting hospital projects, since the latter represents one class of communities in the United States, while the former is irrespective of community size.
** Represents an estimate between two socioeconomic classifications, "wholesale and retail dealers," (5.3 per cent of the employed workers in the male labor force) and "other proprietors, managers, and officials," (4.9 per cent of the employed workers in the male labor force).
*** Represents an estimate of the classification, "other proprietors, managers, and officials" (4.9 per cent of the employed workers in the male labor force).
****Negligible percentage represents an estimate calculated on the basis of 61,712 "county and local," and "city" officials, and a total male labor force of 40,284,000 persons, *Ibid.*, p. 50, Table 2; and p. 12, Table 1.
***** Represents an estimate of three totaled socioeconomic classifications, "skilled workers and foremen," (15.0 per cent), "semi-skilled workers" (18.2 per cent), and "unskilled workers" (23.0 per cent).
****** The difference of 13 per cent represents the classification of "clerks and kindred workers."

TABLE 3

CENTRALLY IMPORTANT SPONSORING GROUPS IN HOSIPTAL PROJECTS

Type of Sponsoring Group	Region						
	South-east	South-west	Far West	Middle States	North-west	North-east	Total
	Percent	Percent	Percent	Percent	Percent	Percent	Percent
Hospital boards or associations	54	64	39	65	51	83	61
Political	38	36	11	19	10	00	21
Service clubs	15	20	29	17	45	00	21
Women's clubs	00	4	00	3	7	4	3
Citizens councils	23	20	33	17	12	25	20
No reply	15	8	28	20	40	8	21
Total	145*	152	140	141	165	120	147
Number	52	25	19	58	40	24	218

* Note: Multiple choice questions resulted in total percentage figures of more than 100. The accumulated percentages are given in this and some other tables because they suggest crude indices of total incidence.

TABLE 4

ORGANIZATIONAL FORMALITIES OF CENTRALLY IMPORTANT SPONSORING GROUPS
FOR 218 HOSPITAL PROJECTS

Formality	Region						
	South-east	South-west	Far West	Middle States	North-west	North-east	Total
	Percent	Percent	Percent	Percent	Percent	Percent	Percent
Constitution	33	28	39	31	38	46	35
Officers	48	48	67	62	65	67	59
Subcommittees for special problems	36	20	33	22	28	46	30
Budget	14	12	11	14	10	13	12
Membership fees	00	4	6	9	15	00	6
Membership dues	8	8	00	10	7	13	8
None of these	2	36	28	26	22	21	18
No reply	4	8	00	5	3	13	5
Total percent	145	164	184	179	188	219	173
Total number	42	25	19	58	40	24	218

TABLE 5

METHODS OF MEMBER SELECTION FOR CENTRALLY IMPORTANT SPONSORING GROUPS
FOR 218 HOSPITAL PROJECTS

Method	Region						
	South-east	South-west	Far West	Middle States	North-west	North-east	Total
	Percent	Percent	Percent	Percent	Percent	Percent	Percent
Appointment by local officials	36	36	33	20	12	8	24
Elected at community meeting	11	20	6	26	40	33	24
Appointed from community organizations	12	12	33	19	25	13	18
Informally through interest (voluntary)	10	12	6	10	5	4	8
Other (miscellaneous)	10	8	00	10	5	17	9
Formal election	10	4	11	3	5	4	6
No reply	11	8	11	12	8	21	11
Total percent	100	100	100	100	100	100	100
Total number	52	25	19	58	40	24	218

TABLE 6

TYPES OF OPPOSITION IN 218 HOSPITAL PROJECTS

Opposition Type	Region						Total
	South-east	South-west	Far West	Middle States	North-west	North-east	
	Percent	Percent	Percent	Percent	Percent	Percent	Percent
Threatened high taxes	54	60	72	64	42	21	53
Professional interest not served (non-M.D.'s)	4	12	28	7	13	4	9
Interest of Medical Practice not served	17	12	00	7	13	17	11
Other (miscellaneous)	4	12	28	12	20	29	15
No reply	2	00	00	2	2	00	1
No important opposition	29	16	11	21	20	38	23
Total percent	110	112	139	113	110	109	112
Total number	52	25	19	58	40	24	218

TABLE 7

METHODS OF FUND-RAISING EMPLOYED

Method	Region						Total
	South-east	South-west	Far West	Middle States	North-west	North-east	
	Percent	Percent	Percent	Percent	Percent	Percent	Percent
Locally led public subscription	54	44	39	71	80	29	58
County bond issue	48	56	22	48	40	13	42
Professional led public subscription	10	00	6	15	15	71	17
Municipal bond issue	10	12	6	19	13	00	11
Cooperative membership	00	12	00	00	8	00	4

(Continued)

Method	Region						
	South-east	South-west	Far West	Middle States	North-west	North-east	Total
	Percent	Percent	Percent	Percent	Percent	Percent	Percent
Hospital district bond issue	2	00	33	00	00	00	3
Other (miscellaneous)	2	00	00	3	2	00	2
No reply	2	4	00	00	00	00	1
Total percent	128	128	106	156	158	113	138
Total number	52	25	19	58	40	24	218

TABLE 8

COMMUNITY APPEALS EMPLOYED IN PUBLICITY
CAMPAIGNS FOR 218 HOSPITAL PROJECTS

Appeal	Region						
	South-east	South-west	Far West	Middle States	North-west	North-east	Total
	Percent	Percent	Percent	Percent	Percent	Percent	Percent
"Making the community a better place to live in"	79	72	83	90	90	79	84
"Health is a community responsibility"	73	76	72	57	62	71	67
Memorial to relative or friend	31	40	17	53	45	88	45
Fear of personal or family poor health	19	28	22	24	30	29	25
Desire for prestige that a contribution would bring	13	8	17	15	30	29	18
"Others support it, why not you?"	6	8	6	8	3	25	8
Other (miscellaneous)	00	4	6	2	00	00	2
No reply	13	8	11	2	5	00	6
Total percent	234	244	234	251	265	321	255
Total number	52	25	19	58	40	24	218

TABLE 9

FINAL OWNERSHIP OF 218 HILL–BURTON HOSPITALS

Ownership Type	South-east	South-west	Far West	Middle States	North-west	North-east	Total
	Region						
	Percent	Percent	Percent	Percent	Percent	Percent	Percent
County	51	44	50	43	40	12	42
City	10	28	00	22	12	00	14
County-City	00	4	00	2	00	00	1
Non-Profit Ass'n	39	24	17	33	48	88	40
Special Hospital District	00	00	33	00	00	00	3
Total percent	100	100	100	100	100	100	100
Total number	52	25	19	58	40	24	218

TABLE 10

POLITICAL COMPONENTS IN CIVIL GOVERNMENT AND VOLUNTARY SPONSORED HOSPITAL PROJECTS

Component	Sponsorship Type	
	Civil Government	Voluntary
	Percent	Percent
Members of sponsoring and/or operating body appointed by local officials	49	20
Bond issue as fund-raising method	63	30
County or municipal hospital ownership	81	41
Low personnel in project (10 or less)	12	13
Total percent	205	104
Total number	46	126

TABLE 11

REASONS FOR PROLONGED DISCUSSION

Reported Reasons	Hospitals	Local Health Departments	Prepayment Plans
	Percent	Percent	Percent
"Not enough money locally"	67	33	35
"No funds available from outside the community"	32	4	24
"Not enough general interest"	27	31	24
"Not enough good leadership"	28	20	29
"No federal financial support at this time"	54	00	00
"World War II"	10	00	24
"Local governing body not sold"	00	31	00
Total percent	218	119	136
Total number	218	51	18

TABLE 12

INITIATION OF COMMUNITY ACTIVITY

	Hospitals	Local Health Departments	Prepayment Plans
	Percent	Percent	Percent
One person	32	18	50
Several persons together	28	18	17
An organized group	12	37	39
All the people together	5	2	00
Business or industry	2	00	00
No response	1	12	6
Total percent	80	87	112
Total number	218	51	18

SUBJECT INDEX

Proficiency: of organizational skill, 17–18, 87, 92, 94, 100, 114, 116, 120, 130, 133, 139, 146, 149–151; of skill with symbols, 18, 120, 152–153, 171–172; of subject matter competence, 17, 92, 95, 99–100, 118, 120, 131, 146, 147–148
Public health officers: appraisals by, 37–39; poll of, 37
Purpose of research, 19

Questionnaire: analysis of, 8–9; construction of, 7–8; mailing of, 7–8; postal card, 10; purpose of, 10; returns of, 8

Region: definitions of, 167; in relation to health, 12, 167–168
Remonstrance, 71, 79–80, 148
Resources: of access, 16, 61–62, 66, 85, 87, 89–90, 92, 99, 107, 112, 114, 118, 126–130, 132, 134, 137, 141–142, 171–172; of "morality," 16, 140; of obligation, 16, 112, 114, 116, 119, 133, 142–143; of respect, 15–16, 61, 66, 126–127, 138–140; of success, 16, 119, 126, 133, 140–141; of time, 17, 24, 145–146; of wealth, 66, 136–138, 146
Respect, 15–16, 61, 66, 126–127, 138–140
Rotary Club, 75–76, 107, 111, 115, 119, 132

Senator, state, 83, 87, 92, 127, 141, 142–143
Service clubs: as sponsors, 23–24; for research, 163
Sex, differential of, 11, 173
Site, hospital, 25, 58, 95, 147
Social movement, 11
Social work, 175
Sociology: of health and medical need, 11, 168; of medical ecology, 11, 168; of medical practice, 11, 169; of mental health, 11, 168; of morbidity, 11, 168; of mortality, 11, 168; usage of health facilities, 11, 168–169
Southeast County: appeals of, 67–68; comparison of, 88, 93, 120, 129, 134, 141–142, 144–145, 149, 151–152, 156; decisions of, 64; location of, 58; political instrumentalities of, 59–61; problems of, 65
Southeast Region: appeals of, 50–51; comparison of, 45–55, 156; media of, 49; political instrumentalities of, 46; problems of, 48, 57; success of, 51–53
Southwest Region: appeals of, 50–51; comparison of, 45–56; media of, 49; political instrumentalities of, 46; problems of, 48, success of, 51–53
Sponsorship: civil, 36, 45; methods of, 43–44, 46, 117; of hospitals, 22–23, 36, 66, 80; of prepayment plans, 36; of public health, 36–37; problems of, 24–25, 26, 37–39, 80; process of, 23, 43, 68–69, 81, 103, 111, 117; structure of, 43, 46, 69, 80, 89–90, 92, 103, 117; voluntary, 45–47
States, relations with, 58, 63, 67, 83, 87, 89, 91–92, 96, 100, 126–127, 134, 142
Status, social, 15, 86, 136
Store, plantation, 60–62, 121–123
Strategy, in decision-making, 18, 78–79, 80, 102, 114, 117–118, 133, 137
Subscription, public, 27
Suburbanization, 73–74
Success, 16, 119, 126, 133, 140
Surveys, 29, 42, 78
Symbols. See Proficiency with symbols